PATTERNS and EXPERIMENTS in
DEVELOPMENTAL BIOLOGY

PATTERNS and EXPERIMENTS in DEVELOPMENTAL BIOLOGY

LELAND G. JOHNSON / **E. PETER VOLPE**
Augustana College   Tulane University
Sioux Falls, South Dakota New Orleans

WM. C. BROWN COMPANY PUBLISHERS
Dubuque, Iowa

Contents

Preface

When one discriminating student in Developmental Biology was asked about prefaces, she replied that she didn't have an opinion because she had never read one in its entirety. She felt that prefaces were generally wordy and usually uninteresting. Developmental Biology is an exciting and dynamic discipline, especially when approached through the study of live material. We wouldn't want to risk "turning off" students and instructors at the outset, but we do want this preface to be read. Therefore, we have included only essential comments about this manual and the approach which it takes.

This manual arose as a product of courses in Developmental Biology which we teach at Augustana College and Tulane University respectively. We make no particular claims to originality of content because the organisms included are widely studied and several of the experiments are used extensively, although others have not appeared in other manuals or have appeared in very different forms. This manual differs from others in the field mainly in its approach to the use of live material and its balance between descriptive and experimental material. Students have the opportunity to examine developmental patterns of four organisms and then to experiment with those same organisms. This combination of descriptive and experimental approaches is characteristic of the methods used throughout the history of Developmental Biology and seems a logical way for students to gain their first experience in the subject.

While the descriptive material is not as detailed as that found in some traditional manuals, the emphasis on work with live material in the descriptive exercises adds greatly to their impact. There is also appreciable reinforcement of learning because the experimental exercises give students occasion to apply their knowledge of developmental patterns. It is not our aim to overwhelm students with excessive factual material. Our objective, rather, is to arouse students' interest in developmental phenomena.

The experimental exercises emphasize work on the organisms studied in the descriptive exercises and are limited to experiments which can be done with general equipment available in most departments and specialized items which can be purchased or constructed at relatively modest cost. Exercises have been chosen on the basis of their practicality for use by undergraduate students with relatively little experience in work with live material and the extent to which they (a) illustrate important developmental principles, (b) introduce experimental approaches to the study of development, and (c) encourage students to think analytically about developmental patterns which they have observed previously. Obviously, no manual in Developmental Biology can be comprehensive, and we assume that many instructors will insert some of their "favorite" exercises as supplemental (or substitute) material.

We hope, also, that the manual will be useful in courses in which students presently have little contact with live material. It can be used as a supplement in General Biology courses, in conventional courses in Embryology in which emphasis has been placed on the study of prepared slides, and in courses in which the subject matters of comparative anatomy and vertebrate embryology have been integrated. The impact of work with live material on the learning experience simply cannot be overstated, and we recommend it wholeheartedly.

Leland G. Johnson
E. Peter Volpe

Acknowledgments

The illustrations in this manual are the accomplished work of Mrs. Carolyn Thorne Volpe. We are grateful for her creative efforts and for the patience and persistence with which she worked throughout the project.

We are indebted to several authors and publishers for their generosity and cooperation in providing certain photographs. Specific credit for these photographs has been given in the legends.

Introduction for Students

Our paramount objective in preparing this manual was to assist instructors in communicating the fascination and excitement involved in the study of developing systems. As a means of achieving this objective we have concentrated on work with living organisms. There is, of course, more potential for irritating failure in any biological study which emphasizes living material rather than dried or pickled, commercially prepared material. However, the potential for exciting involvement is also enhanced and overrides the occasional frustrations that are inevitably experienced. It is possible to minimize, but probably never to eliminate, failures in the laboratory in a course such as Developmental Biology. We strongly recommend careful reading of the general comments on work with living material in the following paragraphs as a means of combating laboratory difficulties. We urge, also, that you read each laboratory exercise carefully and completely before the laboratory meeting in which it is to be used.

We believe that there is high level of regard for living organisms which characterizes most, if not all, successful biologists. This high regard is not related to the mysticism invoked by some persons when they ponder the nature of life, but rather it is a healthy appreciation for the complexity of living organisms. This respect for life normally fosters a very meticulous kind of approach. While we can describe some specific matters of concern in work with living material, we believe that this general outlook is a product of scientific maturation. The Developmental Biology laboratory, with its emphasis on experimentation, can help promote a keen awareness of, and respect for, living systems.

Returning to practical concerns, there are a number of cautions which should be applied to facilitate your laboratory work. It should be emphasized at the outset that the developing systems with which you will work are far more sensitive to changes in environmental factors than are adults of these or other species. This sensitivity may take you by surprise on occasion, and it should be cause for continued care and thoughtfulness as you do this work.

A first rule is that scrupulous cleanliness is an absolute necessity. All glassware and instruments must be as free as possible of all forms of contamination. For example, even minute residues of formaldehyde or other preservatives have devastating effects on developing material. The importance of careful cleaning of all glassware cannot be overemphasized. Glassware cleaners, soaps, or detergents are fully as undesirable as other forms of contamination. Thus, thorough and careful rinsing following cleaning of glassware is essential. Final rinses should always be made with distilled water.

Temperature shocks are to be avoided. Both cold and heat can have adverse effects even if the temperature fluctuation is rather small. Lethal temperature changes are a particularly serious threat in some of the exercises in this manual. Heat death is actually likely to be the more serious problem. Special caution in making microscope observations is urgent because the heat radiated by many microscope illuminators is considerable.

There are other cautions which will be cited in the individual exercises where they are most pressing, but you should always work with the clear understanding that living material is sensitive to chemical contamination, temperature fluctuation, osmotic pressure changes, pH variations, and a variety of other environmental factors. There is a kind of "common sense" which should govern all work with living material and you should watch carefully for potential problems.

In conclusion, we would like to encourage you to read and take advantage of the "suggestions" sections in the various exercises. Hopefully, they will help you to sense the immediacy of studies in Developmental Biology. It is important to bear in mind that most of the information which we currently study and use represents only the present state of knowledge, and that it is constantly being revised as new studies are being completed. Finally, we think that working with developing organisms is fun, and we hope that you enjoy it as much as we do!

Introduction for Instructors

We believe that there is no greater reward in teaching than that derived from watching students "discover" biological phenomena for themselves using living organisms. Because of the dynamic nature of the processes involved, Developmental Biology is an especially attractive area for work with live material, and this manual emphasizes work with live material in the descriptive as well as the experimental exercises. If one appreciates the enthusiastic responses of interested students, the extra effort involved in the more extensive use of live material is well compensated.

It is generally held that work with living, developing material requires very special skills and background. There is an "oral-manual tradition" which is handed on primarily through apprenticeship in graduate-level courses and research in Developmental Biology. Many instructors who will use this manual or consider using it will have been through such an apprenticeship, but others will not have had such experience. This may be because new courses in Developmental Biology are proliferating as a result of curriculum restudy in many biology departments, and frequently the instructors in such new courses are faculty members who had previously taught the more traditional courses (*e.g.*, Vertebrate Embryology) which they replace. We would like to commend the use of live material and a combination of descriptive and experimental studies on the same organisms to instructors who are less experienced in the study of living, developing organisms as well as to those who have had such experience. Especially for the benefit of those with less experience in this area, we have included rather extensive appendix material on preparation for individual exercises and general information on course organization. We also suggest that instructors read the introduction for students.

Observations and Experiments on the Living Frog Embryo

Progress in science is made through observation and experimentation. The continuous change in form of the developing embryo has always held great appeal; and, in former days, students of embryology focused their attention on describing the orderly, normal course of developmental events. A wealth of information was gained by direct observation, often of the most detailed and refined kind. Later, this observational and descriptive work was supplemented by experimental studies. The distinguished German embryologist Wilhelm Roux, investigating the amphibian egg in the 1880s, was one of the first to apply experimental methods to problems of development. From the time that Roux pricked frog cleavage cells with a hot needle, the amphibian egg has been subjected to a variety of microsurgical operations and to numerous alterations of its environment. When an investigator imposes new, or altered, conditions on the developing embryo, the intent is to shed more light on some of the properties of the embryo not revealed under the conditions in which the embryo normally develops. In our study of frog development, and throughout this manual, we intend to combine the descriptive and experimental approaches.

We will begin our study of the frog with a descriptive and experimental examination of fertilization and the early stages of development. In addition to uniting the haploid nuclei of the gametes to produce a diploid zygote, fertilization also initiates the process of development by stimulating the egg to divide. However, an egg can develop in the absence of sperm; such development is known as *parthenogenesis*. The drone-producing egg of the honey bee is an excellent example of naturally occurring parthenogenetic development. Many other eggs which do not ordinarily develop parthenogenetically can be induced to do so by a variety of experimental means. For example, the eggs of frogs, salamanders, and toads may be stimulated to complete the early stages of development in the absence of the nuclear events of normal fertilization if they are inseminated with pretreated sperm which have been

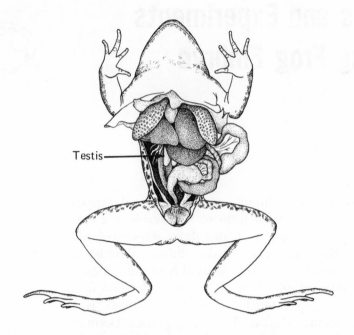

Testis

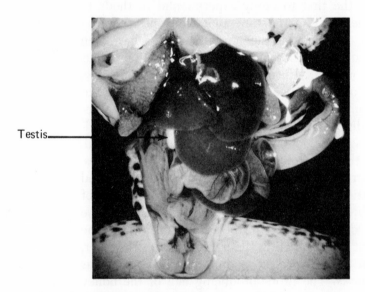

Testis

Figure 1-1. The position of the testes in relation to the other internal organs of the frog.

irradiated or chemically modified. Such treatment disrupts the genetic material of the sperm but does not impede mobility or the ability of the sperm to penetrate and stimulate the egg.

Your initial experience with the amphibian egg (that of the leopard frog, *Rana pipiens*) will be an examination of parthenogentically activated frog embryos accompanied by a parallel study of normal diploid embryos. An embryo which has been deprived by artificial means of one of the parental chromosome complements exhibits markedly impaired development. Simultaneous observations on normal and parthenogenetically activated (haploid) embryos should enhance your appreciation of the complexities of developmental processes in amphibians.

In recent years, the African clawed frog, *Xenopus laevis*, has gained prominence in developmental studies. Fertile eggs of *Xenopus* can be obtained readily, and the embryos can be experimentally manipulated as easily as those of the leopard frog. Although the leopard frog is the organism suggested for this exercise, the African clawed frog is a satisfactory substitute. Techniques of culturing *Xenopus* embryos may be found in Appendix C.

TECHNIQUES

A. Preparation of Sperm Suspension

Mature sperm are present in the testes of male leopard frogs virtually throughout the year (although there is a period of relatively lower spermatogenic activity from late June to mid-September). In common with other vertebrates, the sperm cell (spermatozoon) of the frog is minute, motile, and flagellate.

1. Pith, or anesthetize, a male frog and use a scissors and forceps to dissect out the pair of testes. If you are not adept at destroying the central nervous system of the frog with a needle ("pithing"), then anesthetize the frog in a sealed container with a wad of cotton saturated with ether or chloroform. The testes are yellowish, ovoid paired bodies held to the kidneys by means of folds of mesentery (Fig. 1-1).

2. After removing the testes, roll each testis gently on paper toweling to free the organ of adhering blood and mesentery. Using blunt forceps, mince the pair of testes thoroughly in 10 ml of spring water in a finger bowl. Tilt the finger bowl so that the testes may be macerated easily in the pool of fluid at one side of the bowl. An appropriate substitute for spring water is 10% Amphibilian Ringer's solution (Appendix A).

3. Allow the milky suspension to stand for 15 minutes, during which time the sperm become active. Place a drop of the suspension on a glass slide and examine under the high power of a compound microscope. Observe the shape of the sperm and check for motility.

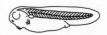

B. Irradiation of Sperm

Nuclear damage is one of the demonstrable effects of ultraviolet (UV) irradiation of the sperm cell. In particular, the energy of UV radiation induces abnormal bonding of the pyrimidine bases of nucleic acids. Thus, chromatin material of the sperm cell is disrupted by UV radiation without diminishing the capacity of the sperm cell to enter the egg.

A phenomenon peculiar to UV exposure is that of photoreactivation, in which the effect of the UV irradiation is perceptibly lessened by the presence of intense visible light (*e.g.,* overhead illumination). Accordingly, it is advisable to irradiate in a dimly lit room. An inexpensive UV source is a 15-watt germicidal lamp, such as the General Electric G15T8 mounted in a fluorescent fixture. The inverse square law operates for UV radiation—the greater the distance, the longer the exposure time required to accomplish the desired effect.

1. Transfer a small quantity of the sperm suspension to each of two petri dishes. The sperm suspension should be spread thinly over the bottom of each dish. Label one petri dish "control" and the other, "experimental." Set aside the "control" dish.

2. Position the ultraviolet lamp 15 inches above the table top. Place the uncovered "experimental" petri dish beneath the lamp and expose the sperm suspension to the rays of the lamp for 15 minutes. Occasionally swirl the sperm suspension gently to ensure equal exposure of all sperm to the rays. Do not expose your skin to UV radiation unnecessarily and do not look directly at the lamp.

You are now ready to inseminate eggs with the "control" and "experimental" sperm.

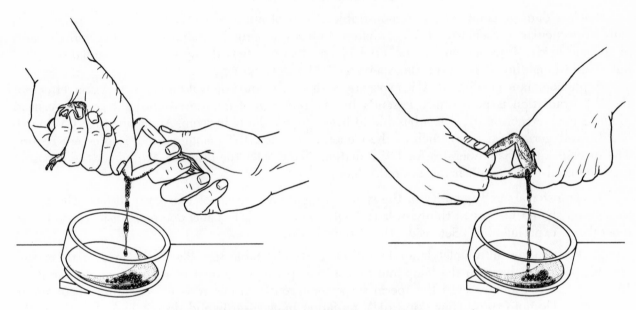

Figure 1-2. Two different views showing the manner of holding the female frog in "stripping" her eggs into the sperm suspension.

C. Ovulation and Fertilization

Ovulation can be induced by injecting frog pituitary extracts or fragmented pituitaries into mature, healthy female frogs. The pituitary hormones cause ovulation within 24-48 hours at room temperature (20°-24°C) or within 4-5 days at 10°C. Injected female frogs will be available in the laboratory. (Pre-injected females can be purchased from commercial suppliers or female frogs can be injected to provide eggs when needed in the laboratory. The procedures for inducing ovulation in *Rana pipiens* are described in Appendix B.)

The female frog need not be sacrificed to release her eggs. Eggs are removed from the oviducts by the technique of "stripping," in which the investigator simulates the role normally played by the male frog.

1. Hold the female frog with her back against the palm of your right hand. Grasp and extend the hind limbs of the female frog with your left hand and place the palm of your right hand over the back of the frog in such a manner that your fingers partially encircle the body just posterior to the forelimbs. The tips of your fingers thus come to rest on the ventral surface of the frog (Fig. 1-2).

2. Eggs can be forced from the cloaca by applying initial gentle pressure to the anterior part of the body and then progressively closing the hand toward the cloaca region. First, squeeze the female over paper toweling until she releases several eggs. Usually they will be accompanied by cloacal fluid. Discard the initial eggs issued from the oviduct and wipe the cloacal region dry. Then, proceed to strip 100 or more eggs into each of the petri dishes containing the unirradiated and irradiated sperm suspensions. When stripping the eggs, squeeze gently and move the female around over the dishes to produce several ribbons or chains of eggs rather than a single heaped mound. To assure complete exposure to sperm, draw sperm suspension into a medicine dropper (or clean pipette) and squirt the sperm over the eggs. Observe the orientation of the black-pigmented area (animal pole) and the creamish-white vegetal pole of the egg.

3. Allow the eggs to remain in the sperm suspension for 15 minutes. After the 15-minute period, pour the sperm suspensions out of the petri dishes, and flood the eggs with spring water (or 10% Ringer's solution).

Note: A mature female frog can release approximately 2,000 eggs. A "stripped" female can be stored at 4°C and she will subsequently yield viable eggs each day for about 4 days. When removed from the 4°C storage, she should be allowed to sit at room temperature for 30 minutes to effect temperature equilibration.

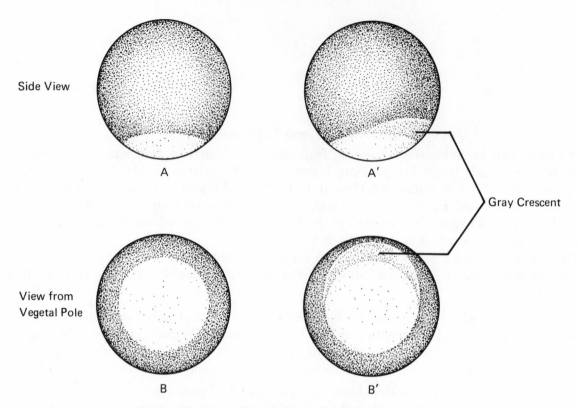

Side View

View from
Vegetal Pole

Gray Crescent

A

A'

B

B'

Figure 1-3. Formation of the gray crescent in the frog's egg. A and B represent unfertilized eggs; A' and B' represent eggs shortly after fertilization.

First Cleavage

Second Cleavage

Late Cleavage

Figure 1-4. The early cleavage stages of the frog embryo.

4. After fertilization, the egg becomes free to rotate slowly within the space (the perivitelline space) located between the egg itself and the vitelline membrane. Gravity causes the vegetal hemisphere containing the relatively heavy yolk to rotate to the underside. Soon after fertilization and before the first cleavage appears, a light crescent-shaped area appears on one side of the egg in the boundary between the animal and vegetal poles. It is difficult to observe this area which is known as the "gray crescent" (Fig. 1-3). The slightly lighter gray crescent area is formed by the shifting of pigment in the egg interior, and the position of the crescent is related to the penetration path of the sperm cell. Since the pigment granules immigrate toward the sperm penetration path, the gray crescent appears on the side of the egg opposite to the entrance point of the sperm. One of the earliest observations made by embryologists is that the gray crescent establishes the bilateral symmetry (right and left sides) of the frog's egg. The first plane of cleavage of the frog's egg, in most cases, passes through the middle of the crescent. Thus, the first cleavage divides the egg into bilaterally equal halves.

5. The jelly envelope, initially dense and viscous, absorbs water and swells to several times its original thickness. This thick envelope of jelly, comprised of two or three concentric layers, serves to protect the egg from mechanical injury. The jelly layers swell maximally about one hour after fertilization.

The jelly mass generally sticks to the glass bottom of the petri dishes. Use a clean scalpel or section lifter to free the jelly from the glass, and, then gently lift the cluster of eggs from the bottom of the dish. With sharp scissors, cut the mass of eggs into small clusters of 5 to 10 eggs. You need not be hesitant or overly cautious in cutting the mass as it is almost impossible to shear an egg because the jelly-coated eggs are very resistant to mechanical injury.

6. Lift the small egg clusters with forceps and place the clusters in each of several finger bowls (4 inches in diameter) containing spring water (or 10% Ringer's). Best development is obtained with 25-35 eggs per 500 ml of solution. To reduce evaporation, cover the finger bowls with a glass plate. No change of solution is required throughout embryonic development. At room temperature (20°-24°C), first cleavage of the egg occurs within 2 or 3 hours after fertilization. The first cleavage furrow begins at the animal pole and proceeds to the vegetal pole, dividing the egg into two equal blastomeres (Fig. 1-4). Subsequent cleavages partition the egg into an increasing number of smaller blastomeres. Other features of the developing embryo will be considered later.

1. Unfertilized

5. Eight-Cell

9. Late Cleavage

13. Neural Plate

2. Gray Crescent

6. Sixteen-Cell

10. Dorsal Lip

14. Neural Folds

3. Two-Cell

7. 32-Cell

11. Mid-Gastrula

15. Rotation

4. Four-Cell

8. Mid-Cleavage

12. Late Gastrula

16. Neural Tube

17. Tail Bud

21. Mouth Open

18. Muscular Response

22. Tail Fin Circulation

   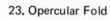
19. Heart Beat

23. Opercular Fold

20. Gill Circulation

24. Operculum Closed on Right

25. Operculum Complete

D. External Features of Development

Various stages of development can be made available at different times by distributing both the control (diploid) and experimental (parthenogenetically activated) eggs to various temperature-control cabinets set at different temperatures, if they are available. The eggs of the leopard frog can tolerate temperatures as low as 6°C and as high as 28°C. However, for optimum development, restrict the range of temperatures from 12° to 26°C.

1. Repeated reference to Figure 1-5 and Table 1-1 will aid in identifying the stages of development. The stage numbers are those originally assigned by Waldo Shumway in 1940. Plan to make frequent observations during the course of the week to witness the continuous change in the form of the embryo.

TABLE 1-1
EMBRYONIC DEVELOPMENT OF THE FROG

STAGE*	DESCRIPTION	AGE IN 18C°	HOURS 25°C
1	Unfertilized	0	0
2	Gray Crescent	1	0.5
3	Two-cell	3.5	2.5
4	Four-cell	4.5	3.5
5	Eight-cell	5.5	4.5
6	Sixteen-cell	6.5	5.5
7	32-cell	7.5	6.5
8	Mid-cleavage	16	11
9	Late cleavage	21	14
10	Dorsal lip	26	17
11	Mid-gastrula	34	20
12	Late gastrula	42	32
13	Neural plate	50	40
14	Neural folds	62	48
15	Rotation	67	52
16	Neural tube	72	56
17	Tail bud	84	66
18	Muscular response	96	76
19	Heart beat	118	96
20	Gill circulation	140	120
21	Mouth open	162	138
22	Tail fin circulation	192	156
23	Opercular fold	216	180
24	Operculum closed on right	240	210
25	Operculum complete	284	240

*Stages are numbered after Shumway (1940).

Figure 1-5. Normal stages in the development of the frog embryo (*Rana pipiens*), based on Waldo Shumway's series.

11

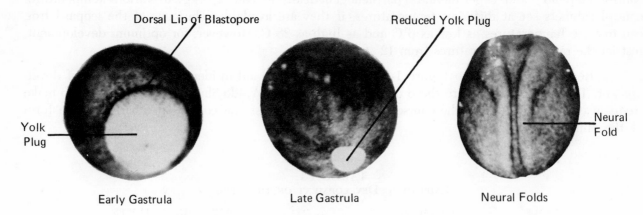

Dorsal Lip of Blastopore

Reduced Yolk Plug

Yolk Plug

Neural Fold

Early Gastrula

Late Gastrula

Neural Folds

Figure 1-6. Selected stages during gastrulation and neurulation of the frog embryo.

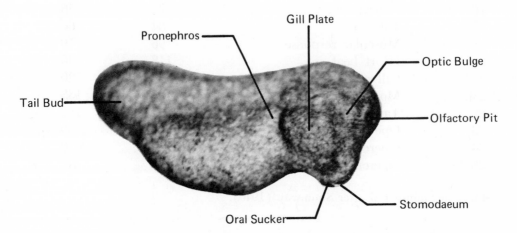

Gill Plate

Pronephros

Optic Bulge

Tail Bud

Olfactory Pit

Oral Sucker

Stomodaeum

Figure 1-7. Features of the "tail bud" frog embryo (stage 17).

The process of development takes place in a series of stages, which follow one another in regular sequence. Segmentation, or *cleavage*, of the fertilized egg leads to the *blastula* stage (stages 8-9). The latter is followed by the process of *gastrulation* (stages 10-12). Gastrulation is a complicated series of cell movements which accomplishes the separation, or segregation, of certain sets of cells, the three germ layers (*ectoderm, endoderm,* and *mesoderm*). Subsequent elongation of the gastrula is associated with the formation of the neural folds and tube (the *neurula* stages of development, stages 13-16). Various outpocketings, inpocketings, thickenings, and other changes lead to the establishment of the sundry organs of the body.

The developmental history of internal structures will be treated in the next exercise; only the external changes during development need to be considered here.

2. Cleavage of the frog egg is said to be *total* or *holoblastic,* since the entire egg mass is divided, notwithstanding the relatively large amount of yolk. Notice that the first cleavage is meridional (vertical); the second is also meridional, but at right angles to the first. The third is unequally latitudinal (equatorial), cutting off four smaller, upper animal hemisphere cells and four larger vegetal hemisphere cells.

After the first few divisions, the cleavage pattern becomes irregular. That is, the mitotic divisions of the cells in the vegetal hemisphere lag behind those of the animal hemisphere cells, which are relatively free of yolk. Consequently, the yolky vegetal cells are larger than the animal pole cells.

3. Notice the external changes that occur during gastrulation. An essential feature is the overgrowth of animal hemisphere cells around the vegetal hemisphere cells (*epiboly*). Gastrulation movements are first indicated by the appearance on one side of the blastula below the equator of a crescent-shaped groove, or depression (stage 10). The depression itself is known as the *blastopore,* and the rim of the depression is referred to as the *dorsal lip of the blastopore* (Fig. 1-6). The tips of the blastopore progressively extend around until they meet, passing through a succession of shapes—quarter moon (stage 10), half moon (stage 11), and full moon (stage 12). At stage 12, only a small area of vegetal pole cells is visible. This remaining visible yolk area is called the *yolk plug.* The ring-shaped blastopore will soon close—that is, narrow to a barely visible slit (stage 13).

4. The body elongates during neurulation, and the neural folds are conspicuously elevated at stage 14 (Fig. 1-6). At the tail bud stage (stage 17), the embryo may be easily divested of its surrounding jelly coats and vitelline membrane. Use two pairs of fine forceps to grasp the vitelline membrane and rip it apart, without harming or distorting the embryo. Leave some of the embryos in their membranes, so that you can determine when hatching occurs spontaneously.

Become familiar with some of the important landmarks of the embryo at the tail bud stage (Fig. 1-7). At the anterior end is the prominent *oral sucker* (or cement gland), a V-shaped groove with prominent lips (Fig. 1-6). Between the lips of the sucker may be seen a depression, the *stomodaeum* or mouth invagination. An *olfactory pit* and the *optic bulge* are evident at each side of the head. The *gill plate* has become subdivided by transverse furrows into three bars, the first, second, and third *visceral* (or branchial) *arches.* Behind the gill plate, a lateral swelling marks the position of the *pronephros,* or early larval kidney. The *tail bud* appears as an outgrowth of the posterior end of the body. Note that the embryo rotates continuously within its jelly coats; the body is, of course, covered with cilia.

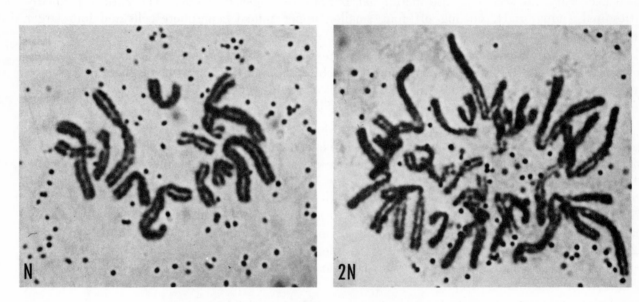

Figure 1-8. Mitotic figures as seen in aceto-orcein squash preparations of cells of the tail region of haploid ($n = 13$) and diploid ($2n = 26$) embryos.

5. Try to detect the beating of the heart at stage 19 by using a bright light source and focusing carefully on the ventral surface immediately posterior to the V-shaped sucker. Look for circulation of blood through the external gills in a stage 20 embryo. The external gills developed as branched filaments on the visceral arches. In late embryonic development, the tail is differentiated into a dorsal and ventral fin, and *myotomes* (or muscle segments) become clearly visible. At the base of the tail, the *proctodaeum* is evident in the place where the blastopore closed.

In the closing stages of embryonic development (stages 21-25), a mouth forms and rows of horny teeth develop. Witness the development of the *operculum* as the external gills are resorbed and replaced by internal gills. These membranous folds (on each side) grow back from the visceral arches and become fused with the trunk, leaving only one aperture, the *spiracle*, on the left side. The spiracle provides the means by which water, taken in at the mouth, passes through the gill slits to the exterior. The closure of the operculum on both sides (stage 25) marks the completion of embryonic development.

E. Haploid Development

Compare the haploid (parthenogentically activated) embryos with control (diploid) embryos and describe any differences which you observe in detail (see Pogany, 1971; 1973).

You may wish to confirm the chromosome number in the haploid embryos. Accurate counts of metaphase chromosomes may be obtained from squash preparations of tail tips of the embryos at stages 22-23. Representative haploid ($n = 13$) and diploid ($2n = 26$) metaphase configurations are shown in Figure 1-8.

1. Immerse an embryo at stage 22 or 23 in 1:3000 solution of ethyl m-aminobenzoate methane sulfonate until immobile. Cut off the distal 1/3 of the embryo's tail tip with a razor blade or scalpel. Transfer the tail tip to a clean slide with a medicine dropper.
2. Remove the solution around the tail tip and add distilled water for 2 to 10 minutes. The purpose of the hypotonic distilled water is to swell the nucleus and despiralize the chromosomes.
3. Draw off the distilled water and replace it with a large drop of a 2% aceto-orcein solution. Quickly add a clean cover slip over the tissue to prevent crystal formation of the stain.
4. After 5 minutes, place one paper towel above the cover slip and exert strong pressure on the cover slip with your thumb. Seal the edges of the cover slip with melted glycerine jelly applied with a fine brush. A comparable semipermanent preparation can also be prepared by using a nonresinous mounting medium to ring the edges of the cover slip. Examine the preparation microscopically for metaphase plates.
5. The slides may be stored in a refrigerator at 2°-4°C. The preparation will last for several days and, indeed, the stainability might improve with time.

SUGGESTIONS FOR FURTHER INVESTIGATIONS

Rugh (1934, 1935, 1937) was one of the earliest investigators to demonstrate unequivocally that ovulation in the frog is regulated by the secretion of hormones from the pituitary gland. The essential features of Rugh's technique for artificially stimulating ovulation in the sexually mature female are described in Appendix B. In 1939, Heilbrunn and his co-workers succeeded in inducing ovulation *in vitro* in the leopard frog by suspending an entire excised ovary in Ringer's solution containing a macerated pituitary gland. Subsequently, other workers achieved ovulation *in vitro,* but it remained for Wright (1945) to provide a detailed analysis. You will find Wright's paper both instructive and interesting. The materials required to repeat his experiment are minimal and you will be rewarded by the simple, but intriguing, findings (see Schuetz, 1971, for references to more recent work).

Your knowledge of artificially induced ovulation and methods of chromosome analysis can be put to excellent use in repeating a short study performed by Witschi and Laguens (1963). These workers found that the ovulated eggs of the frog, if permitted to remain beyond the normal length of time in the body cavity of the female (4 or 5 days), suffer degenerative changes; that is, the eggs become "aged" or "overripe." The aged eggs can be fertilized, but they develop abnormally. The majority of the malformed embryos have abnormal numbers of chromosomes, as determined by squash preparations of cells (comparable to the technique already familiar to you in the present exercise). Thus, a frog embryo cannot develop normally unless it has a full complement of chromosomes, and furthermore, overripeness of eggs is associated with faulty chromosome numbers.

There has been considerable interest among experimental embryologists and developmental geneticists in the effects of changes in chromosome number in amphibians. The extensive reviews by Fankhauser (1945) and Briggs and King (1959) should be consulted. In particular, you might wish to repeat the experiments of Briggs (1947) on the induction of triploidy and the consequences of three whole sets of chromosomes on the embryo. The egg of the leopard frog, when deposited and awaiting insemination, is in the metaphase of the second meiotic division. The entrance of the sperm serves as a stimulus for the completion of the second meiotic division and the consequent release of the second polar body. If, however, the second polar body were retained within the inseminated egg, the resulting embryo would be triploid in constitution. The embryo would contain the chromosome complement of the sperm pronucleus, the complement of the egg pronucleus, and the complement that would normally enter the second polar body. Briggs demonstrated that the retention of the second polar body can be achieved through the suppression of the second meiotic division by the application of high temperatures ("heat shock").

Techniques for parthenogenetic activation of the frog egg in the complete absence of sperm cells are given by Hamburger (1960) and Rugh (1962). These experiments are not technically difficult and you might wish to compare the results with those which you obtained using irradiated sperm. If you do further work with artificial parthenogenesis, you will find the work of Shaver (1953) and Fraser (1971) very pertinent.

Developmental biologists have introduced the nucleus of one species into the egg cytoplasm of another species in order to test the respective roles of the nucleus and cytoplasm in developmental events. Much of the literature on interspecific crosses involving frogs of North America may be found in a review by Moore (1955). Most hybrid crosses result in inviable embryos; some, however, give rise to normal offspring. Among the more interesting hybrids are those which suffer a developmental block at the beginning of gastrulation, such as the hybrid embryos derived from a female *Rana pipiens* (leopard frog) and a male *Rana sylvatica* (wood frog). Such blocked, or arrested, gastrulae have been studied from a biochemical viewpoint, and an excellent summary of this work appears in Lucena Barth's paperback (1964) entitled *Development: Selected Topics.*

REFERENCES

GENERAL

BALINSKY, B. I. 1970. *An introduction to embryology.* 3rd ed. Philadelphia: Saunders.

BARTH, LESTER G. 1953. *Embryology.* New York: Dryden.

BARTH, LUCENA J. 1964. *Development: selected topics.* Reading, Mass.: Addison-Wesley.

HAMBURGER, V. 1960. *A manual of experimental embryology.* Chicago: University of Chicago Press.

HUETTNER, A. F. 1964. *Fundamentals of comparative embryology of the vertebrates.* rev. ed. New York: Macmillan.

RUGH, R. 1962. *Experimental embryology.* 3rd ed. Minneapolis: Burgess.

———. 1951. *The frog: its reproduction and development.* New York: McGraw-Hill.

———. 1964. *Vertebrate embryology.* New York: Harcourt, Brace, & World.

SPECIFIC

AUSTIN, C. R. 1965. *Fertilization.* Englewood Cliffs, N. J.: Prentice-Hall.

ATLAS, M. 1935. The effect of temperature on the development of *Rana pipiens. Physiol. Zool.* 8:290-310.

BRIGGS, R. 1947. The experimental production and development of triploid frog embryos, *Jour. Exp. Zool.* 106:237-266.

BRIGGS, R., and KING, T. J. 1959. Nucleocytoplasmic interaction in eggs and embryos. In *The Cell* (Vol. 1), J. Brachet and A. E. Mirsky eds. New York: Academic Press, pp. 537-617.

DARLINGTON, C. D., and LA COUR, L. F. 1960. *The handling of chromosomes.* London: George Allen & Unwin.

FANKHAUSER, G. 1945. The effects of changes in chromosome number on amphibian development. *Quart. Rev. Biol.* 20:20-78.

FRASER, L. R. 1971. Physico-chemical properties of an agent that induces parthenogenesis in *Rana pipiens* eggs. *Jour. Exp. Zool.* 177:153-172.

HEILBRUNN, L. V.; DAUGHERTY, K.; and WILBUR, K. M. 1939. Initiation of maturation in the frog egg. *Physiol. Zool.* 12:97-100.

HUNGERFORD, D. A., and DI BERARDINO, M. 1958. Cytological effects of prefixation treatment. *Jour. Biophys. and Biochem. Cytol.* 4:391-400.

MOORE, J. A. 1939. Temperature tolerance and rates of development of eggs of Amphibia. *Ecology* 20:459-478.

———. 1955. Abnormal combinations of nuclear and cytoplasmic systems in frogs and toads. In *Advances in Genetics* (Vol. 7), M. Demerec ed. New York: Academic Press, pp. 139-182.

POGANY, G. C. 1971. Effects of sperm ultraviolet irradiation on the embryonic development of *Rana pipiens. Develop. Biol.* 26:336-345.

———. 1973. Growth inhibition in *Rana pipiens* due to sperm irradiation with ultraviolet rays. *Jour. Exp. Zool.* 183:121-138.

RUGH, R. 1934. Induced ovulation and artificial fertilization on the frog. *Biol. Bull.* 66:22-29.

———. 1935. Ovulation in the frog. II. Follicular rupture to fertilization. *Jour. Exp. Zool.* 71: 163-193.

———. 1937. A quantitative analysis of the pituitary-ovulation relation in the frog (*Rana pipiens*). *Physiol. Zool.* 10:84-100.

SHAVER, J. R. 1953. Studies on the initiation of cleavage in the frog egg. *Jour. Exp. Zool.* 122:169-192.

SCHUETZ, A. W. 1971. *In vitro* induction of ovulation and oocyte maturation in *Rana pipiens* ovarian follicles: Effects of steroidal and nonsteroidal hormones. *Jour. Exp. Zool.* 178:377-385.

SHUMWAY, W. 1940. Stages in the normal development of *Rana pipiens*. I. External form. *Anat. Rec.* 78: 139-147.

WITSCHI, E., and LAGUENS, R. 1963. Chromosomal abberations in embryos from overripe eggs. *Develop. Biol.* 7:605-616.

WRIGHT, P. A. 1945. Factors affecting *in vitro* ovulation in the frog. *Jour. Exp. Zool.* 100:565-575.

MATERIALS

Equipment

Wooden-handle probe (dissecting needle) for pithing
Scissors and forceps for dissection
Clean microscope slides and cover slips
"Frog pipettes"
Disposable Pasteur pipettes or other clean pipettes or medicine droppers
Petri plates
Clean scalpel or section lifter
Watchmaker's forceps
Four-inch fingerbowls or other containers for developing eggs (see Appendix A for a source of inexpensive plastic culture dishes)
UV-light source (see section B)
Compound microscope
Binocular dissecting microscope
Illuminator

Solutions and Chemicals

Spring water or 10 percent Amphibian Ringer's Solution (Appendix A)
Ethyl m-aminobenzoate methanesulfonate solution (1:3000 in spring water or 10 percent Amphibian Ringer's solution)
Distilled water
2 percent aceto-orcein solution
Petroleum jelly (Vaseline) or nonresinous mounting medium such as Turtox CMC-10

Living Material

Pituitary-injected female *Rana pipiens*
Male *Rana pipiens*

Patterns of Frog Development

The fertilized egg first increases its surface by dividing into small cells. Numerous cells are thus made available for the initiation of different developmental enterprises. Various movements of cells (and of cell aggregates) in an orderly fashion result in increasing complexity of form and function.

The early period of development is concerned with disposing the cells in the form of layers—the so-called "germ" layers. The *blastula* is essentially the one-layered stage of the embryo; it is later succeeded by the two-layered *gastrula*. As a generalization, the outer layer of the gastrula, the *ectoderm*, is protective and sensory; the inner layer, the *endoderm*, is nutritive. The cavity within the gastrula is the *archenteron*, or primitive digestive cavity. The external aperture of the archenteron (the *blastopore*) marks the posterior end of the embryo.

In some developing eggs (*e.g.*, Amphioxus), which contain very little yolk, the cells of the blastula are arranged in the form of a hollow ball. The process of gastrulation consists of the pushing inward of the large cells of the vegetal hemisphere (prospective endoderm), in a manner comparable to pushing in one side of a hollow rubber ball. In amphibians, however, the presence of a large mass of inert yolk precludes such a simple process of an inpushing of a layer. In fact, the eventual interior position of the endoderm of the amphibian embryo is effected largely by the overgrowing activity of the prospective ectoderm. Basically, the endoderm moves actively to the inside in Amphioxus, whereas the endoderm in amphibians is literally placed inside by being covered over by the animal hemisphere cells.

The close of gastrulation is marked by the formation of the third germ layer, the *mesoderm*, which comes to be interpolated between the outer and inner layers of the gastrula. Each of the three germ layers is defined by its fate in development. The ectoderm contains the material for the nervous system, sense organs, and the external covering of the body; the endoderm provides the

23

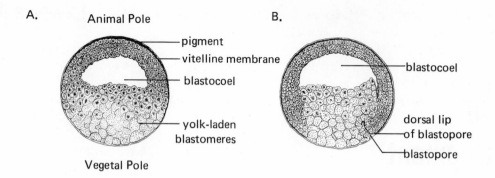

A.

Animal Pole

pigment
vitelline membrane
blastocoel

yolk-laden
blastomeres

Vegetal Pole

B.

blastocoel

dorsal lip
of blastopore

blastopore

C.

Animal Pole

ectoderm (presumptive neural plate)
roof of archenteron (chordamesoderm)
archenteron
floor of archenteron (endoderm)
dorsal lip of blastopore
yolk plug
ventral lip of blastopore
blastocoel

Figure 2-1. Microscopic sections of the frog blastula (A), early gastrula (B), and late gastrula (C).

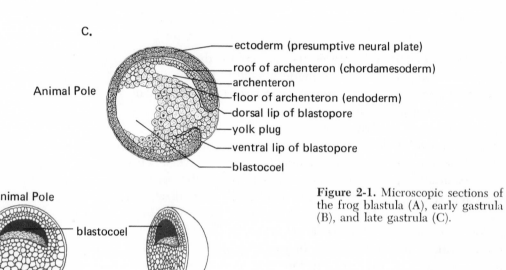

Animal Pole

blastocoel

Vegetal Pole

blastocoel

dorsal lip
of blastopore

dorsal lip
of blastopore

archenteron

blastocoel

dorsal lip
of blastopore

lateral lip
of blastopore

archenteron
yolk plug
blastocoel

dorsal lip
of blastopore

yolk plug

ventral lip
of blastopore

Figure 2-2. Morphogenetic movements of grastrulation in the frog.

lining of the digestive tract and its derivations (*e.g.*, the lungs, liver, and bladder); and the mesoderm gives rise to a variety of tissues (*e.g.*, muscle, bone, and blood).

Embryologists often speak of the *presumptive fate*, or *prospective fate*, of a group of cells. As a result of experimentation, an idealized map can be constructed showing the location of the presumptive fate of a given part of the early gastrula (see Figure 2-9). The orderly migration of cells during gastrulation brings the presumptive regions into their definitive positions in the embryo. Thus, the significance of gastrulation is the allocation of the presumptive regions to their definitive locations.

The external changes in form of the developing embryo which you have observed in the previous exercise reveal only a small fraction of the events occurring internally. The internal processes can be studied in detail when the embryo is prepared for histological study. The embryo is imbedded in paraffin and cut with a microtome into a continuous series of slices, or sections. The sections are stained and mounted in sequential order on slides for microscopic study.

This laboratory period will be devoted to examining prepared slides of various stages of development of the embryo of the frog. Familiarity with the internal changes is essential to the full comprehension of the developmental processes and important for the understanding of the experimental studies to be performed in subsequent exercises.

OBSERVATIONS

A. Blastula

As cleavage occurs in the frog, the egg comes to consist of a large number of cells, or *blastomeres*, which enclose a hemispherical cavity which lies wholly in the animal hemisphere. This cavity is the *blastocoel*, and the egg is now known as the *blastula*. The blastocoel does not arise abruptly; in fact, it may be detected as a small space within the blastomeres as early as the eight-cell stage. The cavity enlarges primarily by the absorption of water from the external medium.

Examine a microscopic slide of a section of the frog blastula. Figure 2-1A is drawn from a stained section of preserved material. The jelly layers of the egg have been removed, and the vitelline membrane may be discernible as a faint line surrounding the egg. The nuclei of the cells appear as dark, dendritic spots. The cells themselves are sharply delimited in the animal hemisphere, but are faintly outlined in the vegetal hemisphere. Note the eccentric location of the blastocoel. The roof of the blastocoel is formed of about four layers of small animal cells. The cells of the outermost layer are deeply pigmented. The floor of the blastocoel is occupied by about 20 layers of large cells, heavily laden with granules of yolk. The blastocoel fluid has been coagulated into a compact mass by the chemicals used in the histological preparation of the slide.

B. Gastrula

Study Figure 2-2 carefully. The illustrations on the left represent the developing embryo cut in the median plane; those on the right are stereodiagrams of the same embryos. The process of gastrulation in the frog's egg is heralded by the appearance of a deeply-pigmented, pit-like depression. The depression itself is known as the *blastopore*, and the rim of the depression is referred to as the *dorsal lip of the blastopore*. The animal hemisphere cells, which have been actively dividing and have actually extended downward below the equator, roll around the lip of the blastopore into the interior. Laterally, to the right and left of the dorsal lip, animal hemisphere cells roll, or tuck, in to establish the *lateral lips of the blastopore*. Accordingly, the blastopore becomes crescent-shaped. As animal hemisphere cells become folded under at the *ventral lip of the blastopore*, the blastopore becomes ring-shaped and filled with a mass of yolk cells known as the *yolk plug*.

The process of gastrulation involves two major types of movements of cells. The overgrowth of cells, or the downward growth of animal hemisphere cells to envelop the yolk-laden cells of the

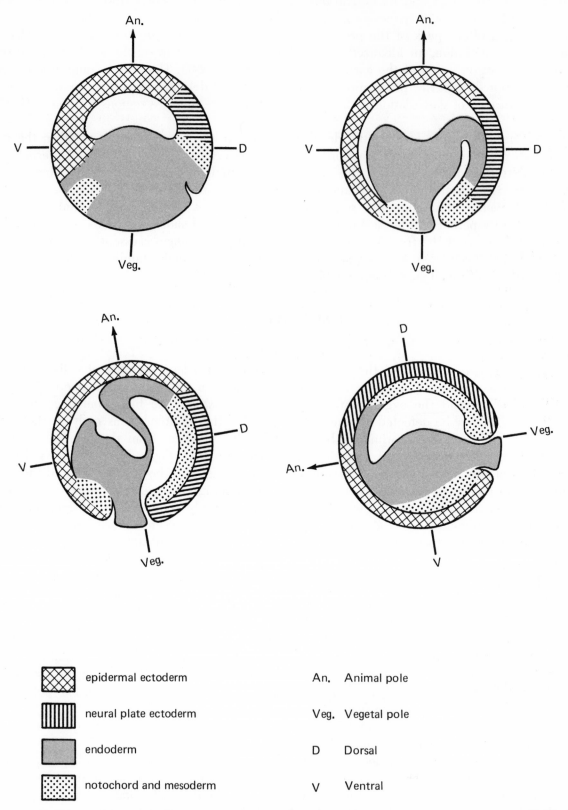

epidermal ectoderm		An.	Animal pole
neural plate ectoderm		Veg.	Vegetal pole
endoderm		D	Dorsal
notochord and mesoderm		V	Ventral

Figure 2-3. Allocation of the presumptive regions to their definitive locations during gastrulation of the frog embryo.

vegetal hemisphere, is known as *epiboly*. The ingrowth of cells, or the inward movement of cells at the blastopore lips, is referred to as *involution*. There is thus a considerable streaming of surface cells into the interior of the embryo.

The sections of preserved material permit only certain inferences concerning the presumptive fates of the materials that become tucked in during gastrulation. The movements of the surface cells can be better followed by staining localized regions of the late blastula or early gastrula. Using Nile-blue as a vital dye, Vogt in the 1920s marked the surface of the early gastrula stage of the egg of the newt, *Triton*. The marking experiments reveal that the animal hemisphere cells actually stretch down over the yolk, and become elongated toward the dorsal lip. The cells become drawn out into streamer-like bands. The cells just in front of the dorsal lip turn in to become the *notochord*, while those to the right and left become the *mesoderm* (pre-somite mesoderm). Hence, the animal hemisphere cells which roll in are said to form the *chordamesoderm*. The yolk cells form the floor and sides of the *archenteron*, or primitive gut. Later, the sides grow up beneath the chordamesoderm sheet to form the new roof of the archenteron. The chordamesoderm thus comes to lie between the new endodermal roof and the outer layer of the embryo, which constitutes the ectoderm of the embryo.

1. Study a prepared section of an *early gastrula* in which the blastopore appears as a small dark notch, and the blastocoel is conspicuous (Fig. 2-1*B*). The blastopore is placed about 25° below the equator in the boundary between the pigmented and unpigmented regions of the egg. Some ingrowth of cells is evident at the dorsal lip of the blastopore.

2. Study a longitudinal section through a *late gastrula* in which the blastocoel is still prominent, but the archenteron has formed (Fig. 2-1*C*). The ingrowth of cells has led to the formation of the slit-like archenteron. Note that the yolk cells have been pushed up into the blastocoel on the dorsal side. The blastocoel is reduced to a small space on the ventral side and will become entirely obliterated. Identify the prominent yolk plug, bounded by the blastopore lips.

Study Figure 2-3 which shows the movement and fate of materials during gastrulation. It should be noted that considerable shifting of the yolk mass occurs, with a concomitant displacement of the center of gravity. The original animal pole of the egg becomes the anterior side of the future embryo, while the blastopore marks the posterior end of the future embryo. With the exception of the yolk plug, the outer surface of the egg is now covered with a layer of cells, the presumptive *ectoderm*. Two regions are distinguishable: the *epidermal ectoderm* and the *neural plate ectoderm*. The future notochord and dorsal (somite) mesoderm are derived from the materials that involute at the dorsal and lateral lips of the blastopore. Presumptive *lateral mesoderm* involutes at the lateral and ventral lips of the blastopore.

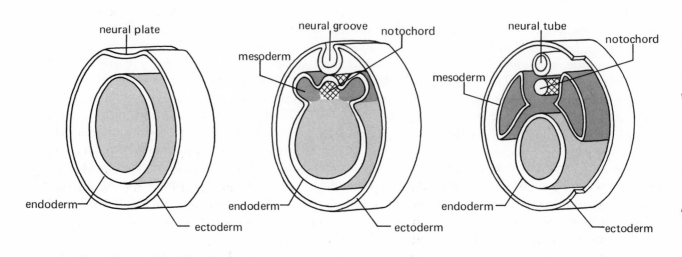

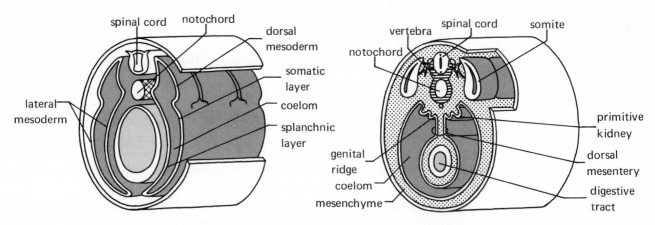

Figure 2-4. Diagrammatic representation of the development of the major organ systems in a generalized vertebrate embryo.

C. Generalized Organogenesis in Vertebrates

Once the presumptive regions have migrated to their definitive locations in the gastrula, the major organ systems proceed to differentiate. Before examining slides of organogenesis in the frog, it would be instructive to familiarize yourself with the simplified and diagrammatic account of the development of the major organs in a generalized vertebrate, depicted in Figure 2-4. Note that the *neural tube* has its origin as a thickened plate of ectodermal cells along the dorsal surface of the embryo. Observe that the mesodermal sheets spread laterally and ventrally around the endodermal lining of the archenteron. The mesodermal bands on either side of the neural tube and notochord, called the *dorsal mesoderm*, become divided transversely into components known as *somites*. The somites develop ultimately into the segmental muscles of the body.

The mesodermal sheets adjacent to the archenteron constitute the *lateral mesoderm*. Each lateral mesodermal sheet splits into an outer *somatic layer*, adjacent to the ectoderm, and an inner *splanchnic layer*, next to the endoderm. The new cavity thus formed, which lies wholly within the mesoderm, is the *coelom* or body cavity.

The lateral mesodermal plates of the two sides grow toward the mid-line, both dorsal and ventral to the archenteron, until they come into contact with one another to form the two-layered *dorsal* and *ventral* mesenteries. Although the dorsal mesentery persists in the adult animal, nearly all of the ventral mesentery disappears; so that the two coelomic cavities become continuous.

Although not represented in the illustration, the mesodermal sheets which lie beneath the pharyngeal floor become involved in the formation of the heart. The splanchnic layer of mesoderm differentiates into the muscular wall, or *myocardium*, of the heart, while the somatic layer of mesoderm becomes part of the wall of the pericardial cavity.

This brief account should assist you in understanding the relationships of the structures seen in sections of the later development of the frog, to which we shall now turn.

A.

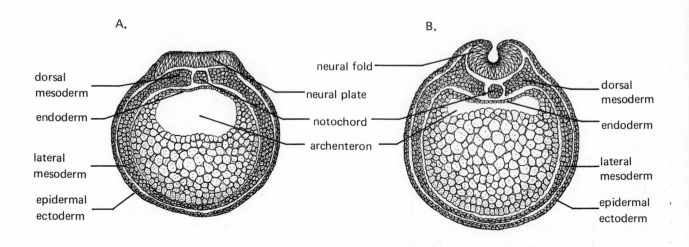

dorsal
mesoderm

endoderm

lateral
mesoderm

epidermal
ectoderm

B.

neural fold

neural plate

notochord

archenteron

dorsal
mesoderm

endoderm

lateral
mesoderm

epidermal
ectoderm

C.

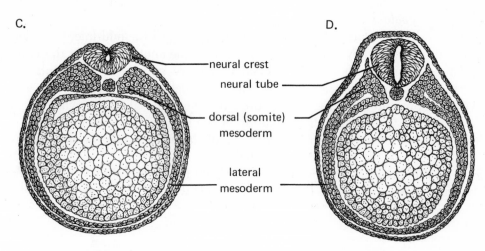

D.

neural crest

neural tube

dorsal (somite)
mesoderm

lateral
mesoderm

Figure 2-5. Neural tube formation in the frog embryo.

D. Neurulation in the Frog

In the living embryo, you had earlier observed that the forerunner of the neural tube is the *neural plate* (Stage 13), which appeared as a faintly-outlined thickening of a wide strip of ectoderm above the notochord. The right and left borders of the neural plate subsequently became elevated as *neural folds* (Stage 14). Finally, the neural folds curve inward and converge toward the mid-line to form the *neural tube* (Stages 15 and 16).

1. Study a section of the neural plate stage, in which the ectoderm on the dorsal side of the embryo is flattened (Fig. 2-5A). The neural plate is actually composed of two layers—an outer pigmented epidermal layer and an inner nervous layer. The former layer is thin; whereas the nervous layer is thicker and is composed of long columnar cells. Note the separation of the dorsal mesoderm which leaves the notochord as a distinct median rod. The future coelom, or cavity within the lateral mesoderm, is not evident at this stage.

2. Study a section of the neural fold stage in which the margins of the neural plate are elevated but the folds have not yet fused (Fig. 2-5B). Notice the endodermal roof of the archenteron, which has arisen by upward growth of the sides of the archenteron.

3. Study a section of the neural fold stages in which the neural folds are in the process of fusing (Fig. 2-5C). Cells which proliferate from the lateral inner margin of each neural fold are *neural crest* cells, the progenitors of pigment cells and a variety of other cell types. You will have the occasion to witness the differentiation of neural crest cells in an experimental situation described in Exercise 3.

4. Study a cross section of the late neurula (Fig. 2-5D). When the folds have finally closed, the outer layer of epidermal ectoderm is detached from the roof of the neural tube. The bands of mesoderm between the ectoderm and endoderm are differentiated dorsally into *somites* on each side of the neural tube and into *lateral mesoderm* enclosing the archenteron. Note the appearance of a cavity within each mesodermal somite. This cavity will close in later development as the somite differentiates into segmental muscle. Theoretically, the lateral mesoderm is composed of two layers of cells which, when separated, enclose the body cavity (coelom). The coelomic cavity is still not conspicuous at this stage.

E. Tail-Bud Embryo (Stage 17, 3-mm)

The tail-bud stage of the frog exemplifies the main features of the body plan of a vertebrate. The anterior region of the neural tube expands to form the brain. Three primary enlargements— the forebrain (*prosencephalon*), midbrain (*mesencephalon*), and hindbrain (*rhombencephalon*)— characterize the cephalic part of the neural tube in all vertebrate embryos. Later subdivisions result in a brain with five well-defined regions universally characteristic of adult vertebrates.

The rudiments of the retina of the paired eyes are outgrowths (*optic vesicles*) of the forebrain, and the future lens of the eye is derived from the neighboring superficial ectoderm. The *auditory vesicle*, which will later develop into the internal ear, is formed, like the lens of the eye, from a thickened patch of superficial ectoderm opposite the hindbrain.

Other conspicuous features, characteristic of all vertebrate embryos, are the *stomodaeum* and the *proctodaeum*. The former is a shallow ectodermal depression which meets an endodermal out-pocketing (the *oral evagination*) at the extreme anterior end of the alimentary canal. The result-ing two-layered *oral membrane* will break through to form the definitive mouth. At the base of the tail, an ectodermal pit, the proctodaeum, will perforate into the hind end of the alimentary cavity to form the definitive hind aperture, either anal or cloacal.

Other organ systems, typical of vertebrates, will come to be recognized as you study the slides of the 3-mm frog embryo.

1. Study a *median longitudinal* section of the 3-mm frog embryo (Fig. 2-6). The three pri-mary divisions of the brain (prosencephalon, mesencephalon, and rhombencephalon) are evident. The prosencephalon is chiefly below and in front of the anterior end of the notochord; the mesen-cephalon is antero-dorsal to the end of the notochord; while the rhombencephalon lies entirely over the notochord. An outpushing in the ventral portion of the forebrain represents the *infundib-ulum*, the forerunner of the posterior lobe of the pituitary gland. The rudiment of the anterior lobe of the pituitary, the *hypophysis*, may be seen as a mass of ectodermal cells dorsal to the sto-modaeal invagination.

The < shaped markings are the *somites*, which formed from the dorsal mesoderm. Differenti-ated parts of the endodermal gut include the *pharynx* (foregut), *liver diverticulum*, *midgut*, and *hindgut*. The hindgut is not readily apparent. The rudiments of the *heart* appear from mesoder-mal elements in the floor of the region of the pharynx.

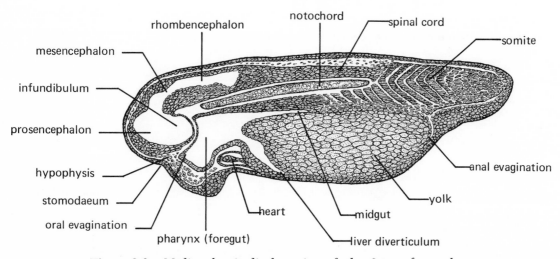

Figure 2-6. Median longitudinal section of the 3-mm frog embryo.

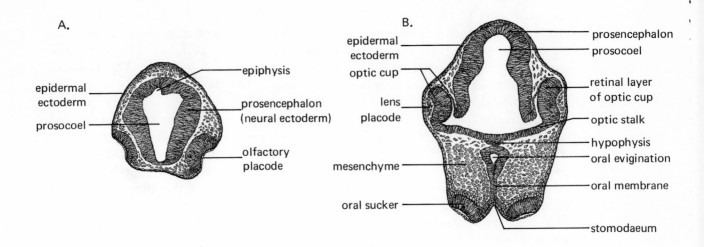

A.

epidermal ectoderm

prosocoel

epiphysis

prosencephalon (neural ectoderm)

olfactory placode

B.

epidermal ectoderm

optic cup

lens placode

mesenchyme

oral sucker

prosencephalon

prosocoel

retinal layer of optic cup

optic stalk

hypophysis

oral evigination

oral membrane

stomodaeum

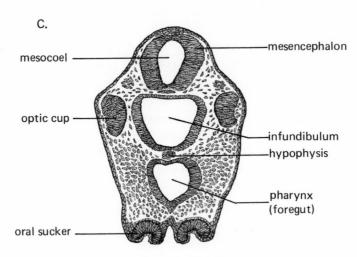

C.

mesocoel

optic cup

oral sucker

mesencephalon

infundibulum

hypophysis

pharynx (foregut)

Figure 2-7. Representative cross sections from different regions of the 3-mm frog embryo.

Continued on page 36.

2. Study *serial x-sections* of the 3-mm frog embryo (Fig. 2-7). The whole embryo has been cut transversely into a continuous series of slices, or sections, and mounted in an antero-posterior sequence on one slide. The most anterior slices appear at the upper left-hand corner, and each row of sections is "read" from left to right. As you observe the structures in each section, make an effort to reconstruct the whole embryo from the various slices.

   a. The most anterior sections pass through the forebrain, or *prosencephalon*. The conspicuous cavity of the forebrain is the *prosocoel* (Fig. 2-7A). Notice that the wall of the forebrain, derived from *neural ectoderm* cells, is clearly delimited from the outer covering of heavily pigmented *epidermal (skin) ectoderm*. Ventro-laterally, on either side of the prosocoel, the epidermal ectoderm has thickened and invaginated to form the *olfactory placodes*, or *nasal pits*. In later development, these pits will enlarge to form the nasal cavities, and will shift away from the surface of the head. The nasal cavities will, however, remain connected to the surface by tubes whose outer openings form the external nares. In many specimens at this stage, you may observe a narrow dorsal outpushing of the brain vesicle. This dorsal evagination is the *epiphysis*, the forerunner of the adult pineal body.

   b. As you trace the sections posteriorly, observe that the olfactory placodes disappear and a cleft appears in the mid-ventral line. This ventral ectodermal invagination is the *stomodaeum* (Fig. 2-7B). The stomodaeal wall meets and fuses with an endodermal outpocketing of the pharynx, the *oral evagination*. The region of contact between the stomodaeal invagination and the oral evagination is the *oral plate* or *oral membrane* (Fig. 2-7B). When the oral plate becomes perforated, the stomodaeal cavity (or *mouth*) communicates freely with the pharynx. Notice the prominent ectodermal elevations on each side of the stomodaeum, the paired *oral suckers* or *mucous glands*.

   Identify the *optic cups*, which first appear as two lateral evaginations of the wall of the prosencephalon (more specifically, at the level of the future *diencephalon*). The optic cup has two layers; the thick (most lateral) layer is sensory and will form the *retina* of the eye. This thick sensory layer will induce the adjacent epidermal ectoderm to form the *lens placode*.

   Beneath the floor of the prosencephalon and dorsal to the foregut, notice the thickened stalk of ectodermal cells, the *hypophysis*. The spaces between the superficial ectoderm and the wall of the brain are filled with scattered mesodermal cells known as *mesenchyme*. Mesenchyme cells give rise primarily to connective tissue elements.

   c. At the level shown in Fig. 2-7C, the brain appears to have divided into two separate parts. Actually, this section passes through the thick-roofed midbrain (*mesencephalon*), represented by the dorsal component, and the ventrally located *infundibulum*, which is an outpocketing of the prosencephalon. The infundibulum, together with the hypophysis, will give rise to the pituitary gland. The rod-like aggregation of cells comprising the hypophysis, previously seen, is still evident just ventral to the infundibulum.

D.

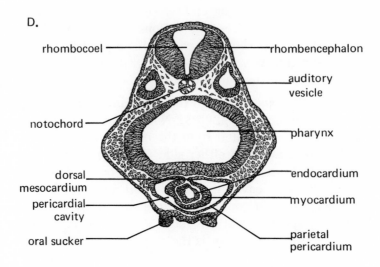

rhombocoel

rhombencephalon

auditory
vesicle

notochord

pharynx

dorsal
mesocardium

endocardium

pericardial
cavity

myocardium

oral sucker

parietal
pericardium

E.

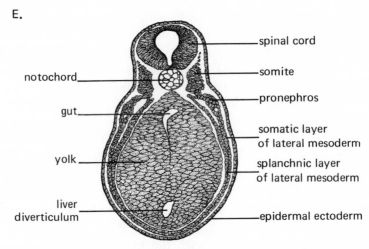

spinal cord

notochord

somite

gut

pronephros

somatic layer
of lateral mesoderm

yolk

splanchnic layer
of lateral mesoderm

liver
diverticulum

epidermal ectoderm

Figure 2-7. Continued.

d. Continue to trace the sections posteriorly, and notice that the cavity of the brain becomes reduced in size and the roof becomes thin-walled (Fig. 2-7D). The thin-walled roof serves to identify the *rhombencephalon* (the future *metencephalon* and *myelencephalon*). Beneath the brain is the conspicuous *notochord,* with its large vesicular cells. Lateral and slightly ventral to the brain, locate paired evaginations of the superficial ectoderm. These are the *auditory (otic) vesicles,* which later differentiate into the membranous labyrinth of the inner ear.

Beneath the expanded pharynx, mesodermal elements have formed the embryonic *heart.* The heart is contained in a large semicircular cavity, the *pericardial cavity.* The inner thicker layer of the pericardial cavity is the *myocardium;* it is derived from splanchnic mesoderm and represents the future muscular wall of the heart. The outer thinner layer of the pericardial cavity, a derivative of somatic mesoderm, comprises the future parietal wall of the pericardial cavity. Scattered within the myocardial cavity are loose mesodermal cells which will soon become organized into the continuous endothelial lining of the heart known as the *endocardium.*

e. Examine serial sections more posteriorly until the foregut is much reduced dorsally and the rudiment of the *liver* is visible as a fingerlike evagination of the ventral wall of the foregut. The liver diverticulum extends into the yolk mass (Fig. 2-7E). On either side of the notochord, the dorsal mesoderm has segmented to form the *somites.* Notice the double-layered condition of the *lateral mesoderm.* The outer layer adjacent to the ectoderm is the somatic mesoderm; the inner layer associated with the endoderm is the splanchnic layer. The cavity between these two layers is the *coelom.*

Between the dorsal mesoderm (somite) and the lateral mesoderm is an area technically known as the *intermediate (mesomeric) mesoderm.* At this stage the intermediate mesoderm has enlarged and differentiated into the *pronephros,* the functional kidney of the larva. The pronephric duct, a rounded vesicle, may be identifiable.

Far posteriorly, locate the *proctodaeum,* which originates as a ventral invagination of the epidermal ectoderm.

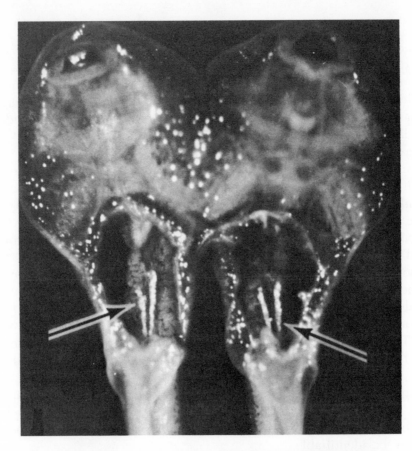

Figure 2-8. The exposed genital ridges of the frog tadpole, showing the light-colored primordial germ cells (indicated by arrows). The illustration shows two tadpoles in parabiotic union; the technique of parabiosis is considered in Exercise 3.

F. Dissection of the 11-mm Embryo (Stage 25)

During stages 23-25, a fold of integument, the *opercular fold,* grows back to enclose and cover the external gills on each side. The resulting gill chamber remains in communication with the exterior through a short funnel on the left side only, known as the *spiracle.* Opercular growth is completed sooner on the right side (stage 24) than on the left side (stage 25). The dissection described below for stage 25 embryos may be performed equally as well on stage 24 embryos.

1. Use a wide-mouth pipette to transfer a tadpole to the anesthetic solution. This is a 1:3000 solution of ethyl m-aminobenzoate methanesulfonate in spring water. Wait until the tadpole stops all swimming and other movements. Then test it for responsiveness to touch by gently poking it with a blunt instrument. When the tadpole shows no response to touch, transfer it to an operating dish. There should be at least enough of the anesthetic solution in the dish to prevent excessive drying.

2. Place the operating dish on the stage of a binocular dissecting miscroscope and illuminate it from the side with a focusing illuminator. Turn the tadpole on its back in a shallow groove which you have prepared in your operating dish. Grasp the skin in the anal region (at the base of the tail) with two pairs of watchmaker's forceps and tear open the ventral body wall. Observe the coiled intestine and attempt to trace its course. The tadpole feeds largely on plants and, like other vegetarians, requires a maximum of absorbing surface. The absorbing surface is increased by an exceptionally long intestinal tract. Note also that great length without great bulk is accomplished by the twisting of the tract into a compact spiral. Notice other abdominal structures. Finish exposing the heart if it is not uncovered and examine it and other organs in its area.

3. Return to the abdominal area and remove all digestive organs from the body cavity. You should now have exposed the dorsal aspect of the lining of the body cavity. Along the midline you can observe the area of the developing gonads, the *genital ridges* (Fig. 2-8). Switch your microscope to a higher magnification and carefully observe this area. The two ridges project into the coelomic cavity, and are covered by coelomic epithelium (peritoneum). Note the large, light-colored protuberances on the ridges. These are the *primordial germ cells* which have migrated into this area to colonize the gonads.

4. Make sketches of your observations on the internal anatomy of the tadpole. Make certain that you record your impressions of the genital ridge area as you will need to examine it again in one of the subsequent exercises. You may have to dissect several tadpoles in order to complete your observations on tadpole morphology.

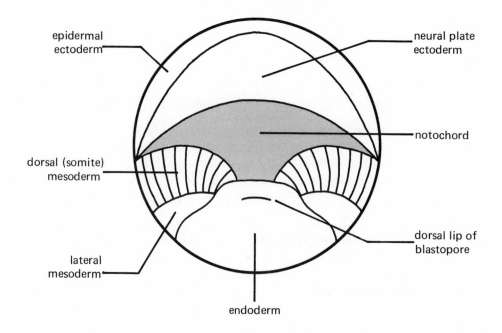

epidermal
ectoderm

neural plate
ectoderm

notochord

dorsal (somite)
mesoderm

dorsal lip of
blastopore

lateral
mesoderm

endoderm

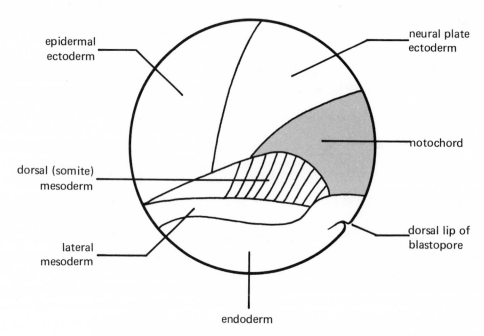

epidermal
ectoderm

neural plate
ectoderm

notochord

dorsal (somite)
mesoderm

dorsal lip of
blastopore

lateral
mesoderm

endoderm

Figure 2-9. A "map" of the presumptive, or prospective, fate of groups of cells found on the surface of the early gastrula of the frog, based on Vogt's experiments with vital dyes.

SUGGESTIONS FOR FURTHER INVESTIGATION

The application of vital dyes to the surface of the late blastula (or early gastrula) by Vogt made it possible for him to ascertain the ultimate disposition of regional elements which move toward certain definitive positions during gastrulation and subsequent development. With this method, Vogt mapped the presumptive, or prospective, fate of groups of cells found on the surface of the early gastrula. A prospective fate map of the early gastrula of the frog is shown in Figure 2-9. It should be understood that there are no visible signs of the presumptive areas in the living gastrula.

The results of vital staining are of such interest that a brief account of the experimental technique is given so that you may attempt to repeat this experiment. The operation is performed in a stender dish which has a base of white agar. With fine forceps or a ball-tipped glass rod, a small depression is made in the agar, which is *slightly* larger than the vegetal half of the early gastrula. The jelly surrounding the early gastrula is removed by "rolling" the embryo in the palm of one's hand. The vitelline membrane is left intact. The embryo is then placed, vegetal pole downwards, in the hollow of the agar. The dorsal lip should be just below the level of the edge of the depression. Finally, a piece of cellophane stained with Nile blue sulphate or with neutral red is snugly inserted between the dorsal lip and the edge of the depression. After five hours, during which time the stained surface cells have involuted during gastrulation, the embryo is removed from the depression. A simple dissection will determine the location of the stained area within the gastrula.

In the very early gastrula, the fates of most regions are not irrevocably fixed, or *determined*. Spemann transplanted a piece of presumptive neural tube material of an early gastrula to a different region of another gastrula. Conversely, he placed a piece of presumptive epidermis into the appropriate region of the presumptive neural tube. The presumptive neural tube material when placed elsewhere did not form a neural tube, but rather produced ordinary ectoderm like that surrounding it in its new location. The implant of presumptive epidermis in the future neural tube area differentiated into neural plate (tube) tissue. Thus, the regions removed from their normal sites develop in harmony with their new surroundings, regardless of their origin and former surroundings.

However, the fate of one region of the early gastrula is determined. This is the region of the dorsal lip of the blastopore, which is destined to form the chordamesoderm (notochord and mesoderm). When the dorsal lip is transplanted to the flank of another embryo, it will self-differentiate into notochord and mesodermal elements. Moreover, the dorsal lip material will cause the overlying ectoderm with which it is in contact to form neural plate tissue (and subsequently a neural tube). In other words, the dorsal lip of the blastopore has the capacity to *induce* other tissue to differentiate in certain directions. Spemann spoke of the dorsal lip of the blastopore as the *organizer*. The action of the dorsal lip in causing certain cells to respond by forming a specific tissue (neural tissue) is known as *induction*. The tissue which responds is said to have a certain *competence*.

Thus, another significant feature of gastrulation in the amphibian embryo is revealed: the dorsal lip of the blastopore is essential for the future formation of the neural tube. A modern review of the nature of the organizer may be found in Balinsky's text, *An Introduction to Embryology*.

REFERENCES

GENERAL

BALINSKY, B. I. 1970. *An introduction to embryology.* 3rd ed. Philadelphia: Saunders.

BALLARD, W. W. 1964. *Comparative anatomy and embryology.* New York: Ronald.

BARTH, L. G. *Embryology.* 1953. New York: Dryden.

HUETTNER, A. F. 1964. *Fundamentals of comparative embryology of the vertebrates.* rev. ed. 14th printing. New York: Macmillan.

NELSEN, O. E. 1953. *Comparative embryology of the vertebrates.* New York: McGraw-Hill.

SPECIFIC

BURNSIDE, M. R., and JACOBSON, A. G. 1968. Analysis of morphogenetic movements in the neural plate of the newt *Taricha torosa. Develop. Biol.* 18:537-552.

COSTELLO, D. P. Cleavage, blastulation and gastrulation. In *Analysis of development,* B. H. Willier, P. A. Weiss, and V. Hamburger eds. 1955. Philadelphia: Saunders, pp. 213-229.

NEEDHAM, J. N. 1942. *Biochemistry and morphogenesis.* Cambridge: Cambridge University Press.

SPEMANN, H. 1962. *Embryonic development and induction.* New York: Hafner. (A reprint of Spemann's book originally published in 1938 by the Yale University Press.)

WILLIER, B. H., and OPPENHEIMER, J. M. 1964. *Foundations of experimental embryology.* Englewood Cliffs, New Jersey: Prentice-Hall. (Contains original papers of the pioneering research of Roux and Spemann.)

MATERIALS

EQUIPMENT

Compound microscope

Binocular microscope

Illuminator

Watchmaker's forceps

Operating dish (see Appendix A)

"Frog pipette"

SOLUTIONS AND CHEMICALS

Ethyl m-aminobenzoate methanesulfonate solution (1:3000 in spring water or 10 percent Amphibian Ringer's solution)

LIVING MATERIAL

Stage 25 (11-mm) frog embryos

COMMERCIALLY PREPARED SLIDES

Frog blastula section

Early gastrula sagittal section

Late gastrula or yolk plug sagittal section

Neural plate or early neural groove representative cross sections

Neural fold or late neural groove rep. c.s. (some companies supply slides labeled, "groove-tube transition")

Early neural tube rep. c.s.

Late neural tube rep. c.s.

Representative longitudinal sections of 3-mm frog embryos or 4-mm frog embryos (selected sections on a "serial sagittal sections" slide can be used as well)

Serial cross sections of 3-mm frog embryos or 4-mm frog embryos

Extirpation Experiments, Transplantations, and Parabiosis

In the very early gastrula of the frog, the prospective fates of all regions save that of the dorsal lip of the blastopore (the "organizer") are not irrevocably determined. Most regions show dependent differentiation; that is, their developmental fate is conditioned by surrounding regions. This has been shown by transplantation experiments which involve the transfer, or grafting, of one part of an embryo to another area of an embryo. Transplanted regions of the early gastrula are "plastic" as regards their final fate. However, after gastrulation has been completed, the various presumptive regions are no longer plastic and, accordingly, they develop by self-differentiation. This, once again, has been demonstrated by transplantation experiments. A piece of post-gastrula tissue grafted into a different region of an embryo does not respond to its new tissue environment because its fate has been determined by this time, and cells of the tissue have become biochemically committed to specific developmental pathways.

It should be evident that an experimental attack—the method of transplantation—permits insight into the influence of one region upon another. Transplantation has been one of the most important tools in elucidating developmental relationships. The transplantation procedures used on amphibian embryos do not comprise ordinary, or crude, dissection, but rather a special kind of "microsurgery" in which fine glass or tungsten needles and other specially prepared instruments are employed.

In this exercise, you will have the opportunity to perform surgical manipulations on the amphibian embryo. Specifically, you will attempt (a) to extirpate embryonic tissues, (b) to transplant the excised tissue to a new, or foreign, environment, and (c) to graft two embryos together side-to-side.

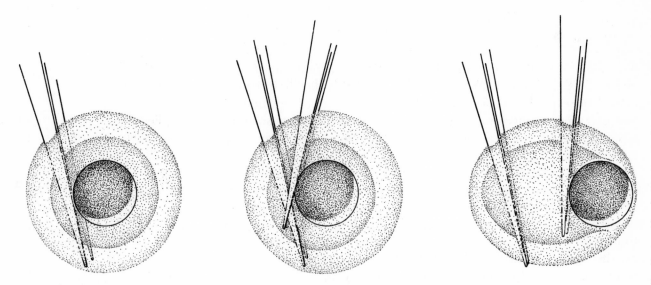

Figure 3-1. Steps in the removal of the jelly envelopes of the frog embryo.

TECHNIQUES

A. Extirpation of a Lateral Neural Fold

Experimentation will consist of the removal of a single lateral neural fold from an embryo at a stage before the folds have come together (stage 14). This type of surgery is often referred to as a "defect" experiment. The ablation of one part, of course, affects the relations of the parts of the embryo to one another. What are the chances of survival of an embryo deprived of one lateral neural fold? Will a complete neural tube form from the other intact fold? Will the proliferation and invasion of cells adjacent to the wound surface restore, or reconstitute, the ablated region to normal form?

1. The operation should be done under aseptic conditions. The operating medium is Barth and Barth's inorganic solution containing 0.1% gamma globulin. The composition of the operating medium is given in Appendix A.

Perform all phases of the operation itself in Barth and Barth's medium as this medium has been demonstrated to promote wound-healing. After healing occurs, however, transfer the embryo to spring water or 10% Ringer's solution.

2. Aseptic conditions must be maintained. Before a glass needle is applied to the embryo, the tip of the needle should be dipped in 90% alcohol and then passed through a small beaker containing the operating medium. Some workers prefer to dip the glass needle in boiling water rather than in alcohol. Tungsten needles, however, as well as all metal instruments, should be dipped in alcohol and then held over a flame. The stender dish, containing the agar bottom, should be covered with a sterile lid (except, of course, during the operation itself).

Agar serves as an excellent substrate for the operations, but it is also a potential substrate for the growth of bacteria. Perform only one operation in each stender dish. After the completion of healing, place the embryo in a separate dish and cover the dish with a lid.

3. With a wide-mouth pipette, transfer a frog embryo in the early neurula stage of development (stage 14) to an agar-bottomed stender dish containing the operating medium. The removal of the jelly envelopes and the vitelline membrane should offer no special difficulties at this stage. Use two pairs of watchmaker's forceps and work under the low power of a binocular dissecting microscope. Pierce the jelly envelopes with one prong of the left forceps, as shown in Figure 3-1. A firm grip of the jelly coats may be secured by closing the left forceps. Then, insert both prongs of the right forceps into the jelly coat closely adjacent to the first prong. Pull the right pair of forceps in a quick motion away from the left pair of forceps. The embryo, still contained within its vitelline membrane, should "squirt" out of its ruptured jelly envelopes. The same procedure is used in removing the vitelline membrane. The vitelline membrane is firmly grasped with the left pair of forceps, and torn apart with a quick jerk of the right pair of forceps. The denuded embryo must be handled carefully.

Steps in Operation

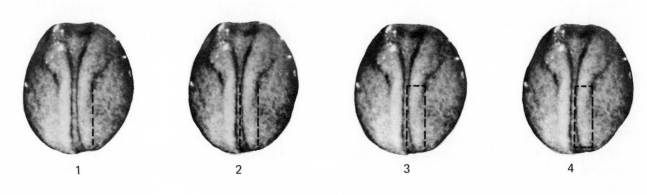

1   2   3   4

Post-Operation 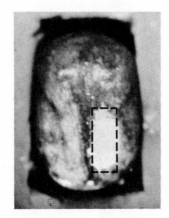 Fold Removed

Figure 3-2. Successive steps in the ablation of a single lateral neural fold of a frog embryo.

4. With a ball-tipped glass needle (or a watchmaker's forceps), make a shallow depression in the agar in which the embryo will "sit" comfortably, dorsal side up. Using a fine-tipped glass needle, remove the neural fold on the right side as indicated in Figure 3-2. With a single complete motion, anterior to posterior, of your glass needle make a thin "rip" in the pigmented epidermis very close to the outer edge of the right lateral fold. Then "rip" carefully through the whitish mesodermal cells until the grayish-tan endodermal cells become visible. Do not cut through the endodermal cells, which comprise the roof of the archenteron. If the roof of the archenteron is injured, discard the embryo and start anew with another embryo.

Follow the first longitudinal cut or "rip" with a second longitudinal cut, at the inner edge of the right lateral neural fold (Figure 3-2). The subsequent two cuts are transverse cuts, anteriorly and posteriorly, thus delimiting a rectangular mass of neural fold tissue. The epidermis has a tendency to peel away from the underlying mesoderm; care should be exercised to avoid loosening the epidermal layer.

5. Lift the entire rectangular area of neural tissue away from the embryo with the tip of the glass needle. The excised piece should include the thick mass of whitish mesoderm with the overlying pigmented ectoderm. The grayish-tan roof of the archenteron should not be punctured during the removal of the mesodermal-ectodermal mass.

6. Leave the embryo in the operating medium until the wound closes over. The healing process ordinarily takes place within an hour. Watch the process of healing. After complete healing, transfer the "half-fold" embryo in a wide-mouth pipette to spring water or 10% Ringer's solution in a glass dish (without agar). Maintain the embryo at lower temperatures (15°-18°C) to decrease susceptibility to bacterial infection. Allow the embryo to develop and record observations of external features of development. Make comparisons with normal, unoperated embryos.

7. As indicated below, amphibian pigment is derived from the neural crest. The extirpation of one neural fold has resulted in the ablation of an appreciable supply of neural crest. If facilities are available, rear some of the experimental animals through metamorphosis and note the possible effect on the pigmentary pattern.

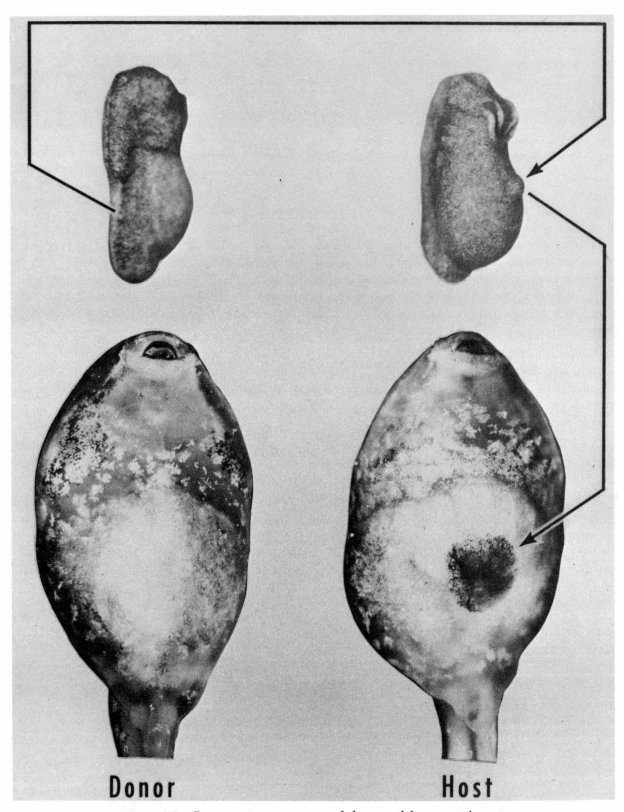

Donor

Host

Figure 3-3. Postoperative appearance of donor and host at embryonic tail bud stage 17 (*top*): a conspicuous feature of the host embryo is the dome-shaped elevation in the ventral surface, the site of the neural fold implant. Self-differentiation of the neural fold graft is evident in the comparisons of the donor and host larvae (*bottom*). The host larva bears ventrally a distinctive circular mass of graft pigment cells.

B. Transplantation

Classical experiments by DuShane in the 1930's revealed that the neural crest elements are precursors of pigment cells. To demonstrate that the pigment cells are derived from the neural crest, we may transplant the crest material to another region on the body. Neural crest cells form a dorsally placed wedge between the lateral wall of the neural fold and the ectoderm on each side of the embryo. Hence, the extirpation of a lateral neural fold also removes a portion of the neural crest. The lateral neural crest elements can then be implanted into the ventral (abdominal) surface of another embryo.

1. As previously described, remove the jelly coats and vitelline membrane from two embryos at stage 14. Place the two embryos, one dorsal side up (donor) and the other ventral side uppermost (host), in shallow, closely adjacent depressions in an agar-bottomed stender dish. The operating medium, once again, is Barth and Barth's solution.

2. Prepare a small "pocket" in the ventral surface of the host embryo. Do *not* attempt to cut a rectangular piece of ventral ectoderm to receive the rectangular piece of neural fold. All that is required is a mere slit, or slight hole, which can be affected by carefully slicing the abdominal ectoderm with the glass needle. The pocket can be enlarged to receive the transplant by removing carefully some of the mesoderm cells with the tip of the glass needle.

3. After you have prepared the host, use the same procedures employed in the preceding section to extirpate one lateral neural fold from the right side of the donor embryo.

4. Transfer the neural fold transplant on the tip of the glass needle to the ventral slit, or pocket, of the recipient neurula. It is not necessary to orient the transplant in any particular direction. Gently *push* (actually, press firmly) the whole mass through the narrow incision and anchor it against the yolk. It may be necessary to enlarge the pocket slightly to accommodate the transplant, but a tight-fitting transplant is desirable.

5. Once the implant has been pushed into the slit, quickly cover it with the flat surface of a piece of a thin-grade cover slip. The weight of the cover slip should hold the implanted tissue in place under pressure.

6. After an hour, the piece of cover slip should be carefully removed. If the transplant has not healed in properly, place it under pressure again with another piece of cover slip for an additional half-hour. After healing is complete, transfer both the donor and the host embryos to a glass dish containing spring water or 10% Ringer's solution.

7. Observe the differentiation of the implanted tissue. Figure 3-3 will serve as a guide. You will observe that in the early postoperative stage (stage 18), the relatively bulky implant becomes evident externally as a moderate bulge in the abdominal region. As the embryo grows into a feeding larva, the mid-ventral bulge will flatten and the graft will become the center of a circular patch of chromatophores, especially melanophores. The melanophore-laden patch will stand in sharp contrast to the silvery adjacent areas of the host. If you examine the differentiated graft under a binocular dissecting microscope, it will be seen that the circular graft area has all the aspects of a transparent piece of *dorsal* skin.

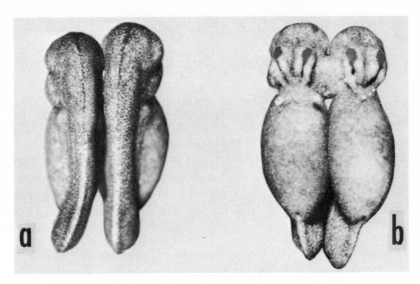

Figure 3-4. Dorsal (a) and ventral (b) views of two embryos in tail bud development joined in parabiosis in the region of the gill primordia.

Figure 3-5. Postmetamorphic parabiotic frogs that had been united together at the tail bud stage of embryonic development.

C. Parabiosis

In grafting two embryos together, various attachments can be made: back-to-back, front-to-front, and side-to-side. However, the most satisfactory position is side-to-side, since this union interferes least with feeding and permits more normal activity. The most suitable stage for the operation is shortly after the closure of the neural folds, when the tail bud is well formed (stage 17). Fine glass needles are used for "cutting," and the operation is performed under a binocular dissecting microscope.

1. Prepare two grooves in an agar-bottomed stender dish containing the operating medium —a shallow depression in which an embryo can be placed on its lateral surface, and a deep rectangular depression with steep vertical walls, so constructed that *two* embryos can fit tightly together (Figure 3-4). The first depression is to be used in creating the wound surfaces in the gill regions of each of the two embryos; the second depression is to be employed to bring the two embryos together in close apposition to each other.

2. After the necessary grooves have been prepared, obtain two embryos in the tail-bud stage of development and remove the jelly coats and vitelline membranes from each. The removal of the membranes should be done in a separate dish, *not* in the operating dish.

3. Transfer the denuded pair of embryos to the operating dish. With the embryo placed right or left side up in the shallow depression, remove an oval area of ectoderm, with a glass needle, from the right gill region of one embryo and left gill region of the other embryo. The extirpated area should cover the entire protuberance of the gill plate. Care, however, should be exercised to avoid cutting the pronephric swelling just posterior to the gill plate. The wounds in both embryos should be approximately the same in extent.

4. The cut surfaces will tend to heal rapidly. Hence, immediately after the patches of gill ectoderm have been removed, slip the two embryos into the rectangular depression with the cut surfaces closely apposed. The embryos should be dorsal side down, and should fit so tightly together that the wound surfaces are in intimate contact. The abdomens of the pair of embryos should protrude slightly above the surface of the rectangular depression. Apply a piece of thin cover slip on top of the pair of embryos. The weight of the cover slip should flatten the abdomens of the embryos, thus preventing the embryos from moving out of position. Recall the strong ciliary movements of normal embryos at this stage.

5. Wound healing occurs within three to five hours. After healing is accomplished, remove the piece of cover slip and gently lift the pair out of the depression. With a wide-mouth pipette, transfer the conjoined pair to a finger bowl containing spring water (or 10% Ringer's solution).

Make frequent observations on the developing embryos and keep the pair alive as long as you can (see Figure 3-5).

SUGGESTIONS FOR FURTHER INVESTIGATION

When you transplanted a lateral neural fold to a different site (the ventral surface) of another neurula, you observed that the neural fold transplant self-differentiated in its new location. Moreover, in the host embryo deprived of the lateral neural fold, a normal neural tube was formed from neighboring cells which closed over the wound. An organ-forming area in the neurula stage of development, such as the presumptive neural fold area, thus has both self-differentiating capacity as well as high regulative capacity. These self-differentiating, regulative organ-forming areas of the early embryo are known as *morphogenetic fields*, or simply *fields*. For example, the presumptive fore-limb area, or fore-limb field, occupies an oval zone on the side of the body, posterior to the gill field. All regions of this field have the power to form a limb when transplanted to another site, and a normal limb can be formed from what remains of the field after removal of part of the limb primordium. You may wish to undertake some of the classical experiments on the transplantation of parts of the fields of the limb, the heart, and the eye primordia. The papers of Harrison (1918), Copenhaver (1926, 1939), and Adelmann (1936) should be consulted (see also Hamburger, 1960 and Rugh, 1962).

A wealth of information relating to the subject of transplantation of embryonic rudiments may be found in Harrison's Harvey Society Lecture (1935). Many of the early investigators observed that embryonic primordia can be successfully transplanted between embryos without any apparent subsequent antagonism between graft and host tissues. More recently, however, studies by Volpe (1964) and Volpe and Gebhardt (1966) revealed that a neural fold transplant in the leopard frog will eventually degenerate. It is now clear that destruction of the neural fold transplant is the consequence of an immune response elicited from the host. If you wish to pursue this kind of investigation, the review article by Volpe (1972) will be helpful.

One of the boldest microsurgical operations, dating back to the beginnings of experimental embryology (Harrison, 1903), consists in cutting two embryos in half transversely and then interchanging the front halves. Anterior and posterior halves of different embryos can be flawlessly united and, as Harrison (1908) demonstrated, such a chimeric embryo can develop into a frog of perfectly normal form. Volpe (1963) employed the technique of chimera production to investigate the problem of the formation of the leopard-like pattern of dorsal spots in the common frog, *Rana pipiens*.

REFERENCES

GENERAL

ADELMANN, H. 1936. The problem of cyclopia. *Quart. Rev. Biol.* 18:161-182, 284-304.

DuSHANE, G. P. 1945. The embryology of vertebrate pigment cells. Part I. Amphibia. *Quart. Rev. Biol.* 18:109-127.

HAMBURGER, V. 1960. *A manual of experimental embryology.* Chicago: University of Chicago Press.

HARRISON, R. G. 1935. Heteroplastic grafting in embryology. *The Harvey Lectures, 1933-1934, Series 29.* Baltimore: The Williams and Wilkins Company, pp. 116-157.

RUGH, R. 1962. *Experimental embryology* 3rd ed. Minneapolis: Burgess.

VOLPE, E. P. 1972. Embryonic tissue transplantation incompatibility in an Amphibian. *Amer. Scientist* 60: 220-228.

SPECIFIC

BURNS, R. K. 1925. The sex of parabiotic twins in Amphibia. *Jour. Exp. Zool.* 42:31-90.

COPENHAVER, W. M. 1926. Experiments on the development of the heart of *Amblystoma punctatum. Jour. Exp. Zool.* 43:321-371.

———. 1939. Initiation of beat and intrinsic contraction rates in the different parts of the *Amblystoma* heart. *Jour. Exp. Zool.* 80:193-224.

HARRISON, R. G. 1903. Experimentelle Untersuchungen über die Entwicklung der Sinnesorgane der Seitenlinie bei der Amphibien. *Arch. Mikr. Anat. u. Entwicklungsmech.* 63:35-149.

———. 1908. Embryonic transplantation and development of the nervous system. *Anat. Rec.* 2:385-437.

———. 1918. Experiments on the development of the forelimb of *Amblystoma*, a self-differentiating equipotential system. *Jour. Exp. Zool.* 25:413-461.

NIU, M. C. 1947. The axial organization of the neural crest, studied with particular reference to its pigmentary component. *Jour. Exp. Zool.* 105:79-102.

TWITTY, V. C. 1945. The developmental analysis of specific pigment patterns. *Jour. Exp. Zool.* 100:141-178.

VOLPE, E. P. 1963. Interplay of mutant and wild-type pigment cells in chimeric leopard frogs. *Develop. Biol.* 8:205-221.

———. 1964. Fate of neural crest homotransplants in pattern mutants of the leopard frog. *Jour. Exp. Zool.* 157:179-196.

VOLPE, E. P., and GEBHARDT, B. M. 1965. Effect of dosage on the survival of embryonic homotransplants in the leopard frog, *Rana pipiens. Jour. Exp. Zool.* 160:11-28.

MATERIALS

EQUIPMENT

Glass microsurgical needles
Watchmaker's forceps
Agar-bottom operating dishes (see Appendix A) with lids
Ball-tipped glass needle (optional)
"Frog" pipette
Binocular dissecting microscope
Illuminator
Pieces of thin-grade cover slips

SOLUTIONS AND CHEMICALS

Barth and Barth's operating medium
Spring water or 10 percent Ringer's solution
90 percent ethyl alcohol

LIVING MATERIAL

Stage 14 *Rana pipiens* embryos (for extirpation and transplantation experiments)
Stage 17 *Rana pipiens* embryos (for parabiosis experiment)

Dissociation and Reaggregation of Amphibian Embryonic Cells

Many developmental studies have concentrated on the behavior of individual cells which have been isolated from their normal tissue relationships through various dissociation techniques. An early report of such work was Wilson's (1907) study of the reaggregation of mechanically dissociated sponge cells. He found that sponges could be cut up and squeezed through cloth to separate individual cells from one another and from skeletal material. These isolated individual cells moved about actively on the floor of seawater-containing vessels and aggregated into clumps of cells. These clumps ultimately underwent internal reorganization and differentiation to form functional miniature sponges.

Holtfreter and his co-workers have conducted a series of experiments (*e.g.*, Holtfreter, 1939, 1946; Townes and Holtfreter, 1955) on the activity of amphibian cells dissociated from early developmental stages. They observed continued movement of cells within reaggregated clusters. This movement resulted in a sorting of cells which ended with specific types of cells localized in specific areas of the aggregates. The sorting behavior of various cell types was based upon the tissue type or embryonic area from which the cells were originally derived. They called this tissue-type sorting process "tissue affinity."

Moscona has worked extensively with dissociated cells of embryonic birds and mammals and has contributed a great deal to our understanding of behavioral properties of embryonic cells. For instance, he demonstrated that cells dissociated during early stages of organ formation sorted out in reaggregates and participated in further development with other cells on the basis of tissue type rather than on the basis of species. Thus, chick cartilage cells reaggregated readily with mouse cartilage cells and cooperated in the production of a cartilage with the two cell types randomly dispersed in a common, continuous matrix. On the other hand, a mixture of chick cartilage and chick liver cells resulted in aggregates in which there was sorting into discrete cartilage and liver areas without any apparent intermingling of cell types.

It would be very difficult and costly to duplicate the conditions used in experiments such as those of Moscona, but it is somewhat easier to use amphibian material to introduce techniques used in dissociation studies. Amphibian cells have a wider range of temperature tolerance; and because of their yolk content, they need not be provided with elaborate nutrient media which also provide good growth conditions for a variety of microbes. Rugh (1962) states a preference for urodelan embryos over anuran embryos in single cell studies, but the culture techniques of Jones and Elsdale (1963) give good results with several species of anurans. They obtained good reaggregation and later differentiation using Steinberg's physiological salt solution supplemented with serum protein. Egg albumin has been used as a substitute for the serum proteins, and it will be used in your medium.

TECHNIQUES

A. Dissociation of Embryonic Cells

1. Obtain a cluster of frog embryos in the late blastula or early gastrula stage of development. With forceps, remove one embryo from the cluster and immerse it in 70% ethyl alcohol for *five seconds* only. This treatment will tend to reduce the number of surface bacteria adhering to the jelly coat without adversely affecting the embryo. Immediately rinse off the alcohol by dipping the embryo in sterile Steinberg's solution and then transfer the embryo to another container of Steinberg's solution.

2. Working under a binocular dissecting microscope, remove the jelly coats and vitelline membrane with watchmaker's forceps as described in Exercise 3 (refer again to Figure 3-1). Alternatively, it is possible to proceed by dejelling the embryo using the "hand" method of rolling an egg around the palm of one hand with a forceps or the index finger of the other hand. The jelly coat will stick to your hand, and you will be able to remove most of the jelly by continued rolling (see Exercise 5). Carefully swab your hands with 70% alcohol and allow them to dry before handling eggs.

3. Use a "frog" pipette to transfer the embryo to a small volume (2-3 ml) of disaggregating (dissociating) medium in a small container. This medium is Steinberg's solution free of calcium and magnesium ions and containing 30 mg of EDTA (versene) per liter. If you used the "hand" dejelling technique, you will need to break the vitelline membrane after this transfer. Sometimes it is helpful to hold the embryo firmly by applying gentle suction with a Pasteur pipette. With the embryo thus held in place, it is relatively easy to tear the vitelline membrane open with a watchmaker's forceps. The cells of the embryo should begin to fall apart within a short time, but the process can be aided by gentle manipulation with watchmaker's forceps or by squirting the embryo in and out of a pipette.

B. Preparation of Cultures

1. Dissociated cells can be collected from the bottom of the dissociating vessel in a clean Pasteur pipette. A washing step in which the cells are transferred to fresh Steinberg's solution may be inserted at this point or the cells may be transferred directly to reaggregating medium if the volume of disaggregating medium transferred along with the cells is kept at a minimum. For observation of reaggregation, cells should be transferred to reaggregating medium in flat-bottomed well slides or to the surface of round cover slips in small stender dishes containing reaggregating medium. Transfer enough cells to give a rather sparse scattering of cells on the floor of the culture.

2. Set a cover slip over the top of each well slide. Prewetting the cover slips by dipping them in Steinberg's solution will help to prevent fogging which interferes with later observations. An-

other method for prevention of fogging is to fill the culture chambers completely so that the cover slips actually touch the medium. Drying will be prevented if you place a thin coat of vaseline around the rim of the well before putting the cover slip in place. Set the preparation on the stage of a compound microscope and focus the scanning objective on the cells. Try to disturb the cultures as little as possible during subsequent observations. If enough microscopes are available, set up several cultures on the stages of compound microscopes. You can observe additional cultures set on the stage of a binocular dissecting microscope. This will be a less satisfactory way to observe cell behavior, but you may be able to detect reaggregation in these cultures also. In all cases, prevent overheating of the cultures by turning on microscope lamps or illuminators only when you are making observations. You may need to dissociate several embryos in order to set up the number of cultures which you want.

C. Analysis of Results

1. Observe the process of reaggregation during the next few hours. There are several aspects of cell activity for which you might watch. Internal cytoplasmic streaming, cyclosis, is frequently observed in dissociated cells as is the extension of cell surface protrusions. Watch for cell movement and the organization of cell clusters. Sometimes linear clumps or chains of cells form as a stage of reaggregation. You may consider reaggregation to be complete when smooth dark clusters have been formed.

2. Record the events of reaggregation including various cellular activities. Note the stages of the process and the time course of the process as well as any other observations which you might make. One technique for recording results might be sketching microscope fields of view at various time intervals.

3. You may elect to maintain your cultures for several days in an attempt to observe differentiative changes in the appearance of cells over a period of time. Maintain the cultures at room temperature, and avoid contamination by covering the microscope with a shield of transparent plastic sheeting. After 5 or 6 days, you may observe evidences of histological differentiation of some cells.

SUGGESTIONS FOR FURTHER INVESTIGATIONS

The original sponge reaggregation experiments are interesting to repeat and can be spectacularly extended by mixing cells from two species of sponges which differ in pigmentation. Tom Humphreys has used sponge cells to examine the mechanism of cell aggregation. His work is also of interest because he uses techniques developed in the Moscona laboratory such as rotating cultures which permit greater repeatability of reaggregation experiments (see Humphreys, 1963).

Jones and Elsdale (1963) found that the ultimate course of differentiation of reaggregated cells was altered if the protein component of the medium was subjected to heating prior to use. Comparison of differentiation following reaggregation in media containing heated or unheated egg albumen should be made. The original report of the use of egg albumen in reaggregation medium (Bradfield, 1967) indicated that there was a concentration effect. The relationship of concentration of albumen to the rate of reaggregation should be studied further. You also may wish to compare the techniques of Barth and Barth (1959) with those of Jones and Elsdale.

Giudice (1962) dissociated the cells of sea urchin embryos and found that they would reaggregate and reorganize the general framework of embryos (see also Giudice and Mutolo, 1970; Timourian, Clothier, and Watchmaker, 1973).

Another interesting extension of the dissociation studies is the work of Weiss and Andres (1952). They dissociated (by grinding up!) tissues from young chick embryos of pigmented breeds and injected the cells into blood vessels of older embryos. They interpreted their results as indicating that cells disseminated by the vascular route selectively lodged on the basis of tissue type in the organs

of the host. Their interpretation was based largely on the fate of pigment cells and the makeup of small, disorganized growths (teratomas) which developed in extraembryonic areas of the host embryos (see Andres, 1953). These interpretations have been challenged (Burdick, 1968), and there is still room for experimentation in this field.

Some workers claim that experiments with dissociated chick cells *in vitro* (see Introduction) actually can be repeated under fairly crude conditions, if one is moderately careful and slightly lucky. It is also possible to culture dissociated chick cells on the chorio-allantoic membrane and thereby bypass some complicated *in vitro* techniques (see Suggestions in Exercise 8).

Malcolm Steinberg has published several works on proposed mechanisms of cell reaggregation and sorting (*e.g.*, Steinberg, 1963, 1970). His hypotheses concerning mechanisms differ somewhat from those of Moscona, and they make interesting, but difficult reading. Moscona's conclusions concerning cell sorting on the basis of type of tissue rather than the species of embryo from which they originated have also been challenged, and data indicating cell sorting on the basis of species of origin have been presented by Burdick and Steinberg (1969).

REFERENCES

GENERAL

CURTIS, A. S. G. 1962. Cell contact and adhesion. *Biol. Rev.* 37:82-129.

———. 1970. On the occurrence of specific adhesion between cells. *Jour. Embryol. Exp. Morph.* 23:253-272.

MOSCONA, A. 1959. Tissues from dissociated cells. *Sci. Amer.* May: 132-144.

———. 1961 How cells associate. *Sci. Amer.* Sept.:142-162.

RUGH, R. 1962. *Experimental embryology.* 3rd ed. Minneapolis: Burgess.

STEINBERG, M. S. 1963. Reconstruction of tissues by dissociated cells. *Science* 141:401-408. (Reprinted in *Molecular and Cellular Aspects of Development*, E. Bell ed. New York: Harper and Row, 1967).

———. 1970. Does differential adhesion govern self-assembly processes in histogenesis? Equilibrium configurations and the emergence of a hierarchy among populations of embryonic cells. *Jour. Exp. Zool.* 173:395-434.

SPECIFIC

ANDRES, G. 1953. Experiments on the fate of embryonic cells (chick) disseminated by the vascular route. Part II. Teratomas. *Jour. Exp. Zool.* 122:507-540.

BARTH, L. G., and BARTH, L. J. 1959. Differentiation of cells of the *Rana pipiens* gastrula in unconditioned medium. *Jour. Embryol. Exp. Morph.* 7:210-222.

BRADFIELD, B. 1967. The use of egg white as a protein additive in medium for embryonic frog cell reaggregation. *Proc. S. D. Acad. Sci.* 46:259-260.

BURDICK, M. L. 1968. A test of the capacity of chick embryo cells to home after vascular dissemination. *Jour. Exp. Zool.* 167:1-19.

BURDICK, M. L., and STEINBERG, M. S. 1969. Embryonic cell adhesiveness: do species differences exist among warm-blooded vertebrates? *Proc. Nat. Acad. Sci.* 63:1169-1173.

GIUDICE, G. 1962. Restitution of whole larvae from disaggregated cells of sea urchin embryos. *Develop. Biol.* 5:402-411.

GIUDICE, G., and MUTOLO, V. 1970. Reaggregation of dissociated cells of sea urchin embryos. *Advances in Morphogenesis* 8:115-158.

HOLTFRETER, J. 1939. Gewebeaffinität, ein Mittel der embryonalen Formbildung. *Arch. f. exp. Zellforsch.* 23:169-209. (Translated and reprinted in *Foundations of Experimental Embryology*, B. H. Willier and J. M. Oppenheimer eds. Englewood Cliffs, New Jersey: Prentice-Hall, 1964.)

———. 1946. Structure, motility and locomotion in isolated embryonic amphibian cells. *Jour. Morph.* 79: 27-63.

HUMPHREYS, T. 1963. Chemical dissolution and *in vitro* reconstruction of sponge cell adhesions: isolation and functional demonstration of the components involved. *Develop. Biol.* 8:27-47. (Reprinted in *Molecular and Cellular Aspects of Development*, E. Bell ed. New York: Harper and Row. 1967.)

Jones, K. W., and Elsdale, T. R. 1963. The culture of small aggregates of amphibian embryonic cells *in vitro*. *Jour. Embryol. Exp. Morph.* 11:135-154.

Moscona, A. 1952a. Cell suspensions from organ rudiments of chick embryos. *Exp. Cell Res.* 3:535-539.

———. 1952b. The dissociation and aggregation of cells from organ rudiments of the early chick embryo. *Jour. Anat.* 86:287-301.

———. 1956. Development of heterotypic combinations of dissociated embryonic chick cells. *Proc. Soc. Exp. Biol. Med.* 92:410-416.

———. 1957. The development *in vitro* of chimeric aggregates of dissociated chick and mouse cells. *Proc. Nat. Acad. Sci.* 43:184-194. (Reprinted in *Molecular and Cellular Aspects of Development,* E. Bell ed. New York: Harper and Row, 1967.)

Timourian, H., Clothier, G., and Watchmaker, G. 1973. Reaggregation of sea urchin blastula cells. I. Intrinsic differences in the blastula cells. *Develop. Biol.* 31:252-263.

Townes, P. L., and Holtfreter, J. 1955. Directed movements and selective adhesion of embryonic amphibian cells. *Jour. Exp. Zool.* 128:53-120. (Reprinted in *Molecular and Cellular Aspects of Development,* E. Bell ed. New York: Harper and Row, 1967.)

Weiss, P., and Andres, G. 1952. Experiments on the fate of embryonic cells (chick) disseminated by the vascular route. *Jour. Exp. Zool.* 121:449-488.

Wilson, H. V. 1907. On some phenomena of coalescence and regeneration in sponges. *Jour. Exp. Zool.* 5:245-258.

MATERIALS

Equipment
Watchmaker's forceps
"Frog pipette"
Clean, disposable Pasteur pipettes
Glass well culture slides (Plastic culture slides or cover slips set in small petri plates may be substituted —see techniques section)
Cover slips
Binocular dissecting microscope
Illuminator
Compound microscopes

Solutions and Chemicals
70% ethyl alcohol
Steinberg's solution
Disaggregating solution
Reaggregating solution

Living Material
Late blastula or early gastrula frog embryos (see techniques in Exercise 1)

The Primordial Germ Cells of the Frog

In the historically important theory of the germ plasm, August Weismann conceived of the organism as consisting of two discrete, if not, opposing portions—a *germ plasm,* which functions as a hereditary vehicle and is passed on from one generation to the next, and the *soma,* or *somatoplasm,* which is the remainder of the organism's body and is concerned solely with the individual's well-being. Weismann's concept provided an important stimulus for numerous attempts to trace the developmental origin of the *primordial germ cells,* the forerunners of the egg and sperm, back to the early blastomeres; that is, earlier than the period in which they can be recognized as part of the developing gonads (genital ridges) of the late embryo. In the cases of several invertebrates and vertebrates, it was discovered that the antecedents of the primordial germ cells could be recognized in the late cleavage stages, and even as early as the first division of the fertilized egg.

In 1934, Bounoure, as a result of observations on the European frog, *Rana temporaria,* traced the developmental history of the germ cells back to the fertilized egg. Special staining techniques applied to the cleaving egg revealed that a specific portion of the cortical cytoplasm in the vegetal hemisphere had an affinity for the specific dyes. This specially staining cortical cytoplasm was designated "germinal plasm," and was shown to become localized subsequently in the primordial germ cells. Bounoure's findings were confirmed more recently by Blackler (1958) who demonstrated the unique staining response of the germinal plasm in the vegetal area to the dye, Azure A. During cleavage, the specially staining cytoplasm becomes incorporated into cells near the floor of the blastocoel; these cells, in turn, migrate away from their endodermal location in later development to become localized in the definitive gonads.

A series of experiments involving surgical removal or ultra-violet irradiation have established that extirpation or inactivation of the vegetal hemisphere of fertilized egg results in the formation

69

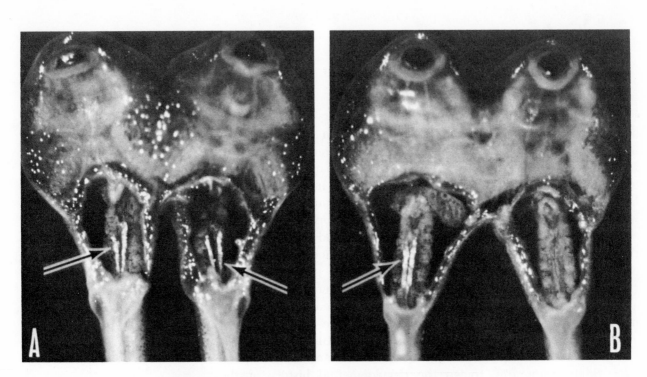

Figure 5-1. (A) Unirradiated parabionts at Shumway stage 25; both embryos possess two conspicuous rows of whitish, large, primordial germ cells (indicated by arrows). (B) Irradiated embryo (right), devoid of primordial germ cells, joined to an unirradiated embryo (left) having two prominent rows of germ cells.

of gonads which lack primordial germ cells. The definitive experiments in determining dosages of ultraviolet irradiation needed to produce sterile gonads and the action spectra of various wavelengths of ultraviolet light were reported by L. D. Smith in 1966. This exercise is designed to repeat some of the UV irradiation experiments of Smith. Fortunately, the results of manipulation of the "germinal plasm" can be obtained by direct visual observation of the genital ridge of the stage 25 tadpole. The primordial germ cells appear as distinct, light-colored protuberances (see Fig. 5-1) which can be observed with a binocular dissecting microscope. Thus, it is relatively easy to assess the results of any experiment which might affect the population of germ cells in the developing gonads simply by dissecting the tadpole at stage 25.

TECHNIQUES

A. Irradiation

1. Obtain frog gametes using the techniques which you have learned previously and proceed with fertilization. When the eggs have been flooded with fresh spring water (15-20 minutes after fertilization), work quickly to remove the jelly coats which surround them. The jelly coats must be removed because they would absorb UV radiation strongly enough to prevent it from reaching the egg. It is possible to dissect the jelly coats off the egg by careful manipulation under the binocular microscope with two pairs of watchmaker's forceps. For an inexperienced worker, however, this is often a frustrating and tedious task and might take more time than you can afford in this experiment. An alternative technique is to place an individual egg cut loose from the egg mass on the palm of one hand. Then use either a forceps or the index finger of the other hand to roll the egg around your hand gently. The jelly coat will stick to your hand, and by careful movement of the egg, you will be able to get most of the jelly off in a short time. You should get the knack and develop your own techniques by the second or third attempt. Quickly place dejelled eggs in a separate container of spring water. Discard any eggs that appear to be ruptured or damaged in any other way. Dejell as many eggs as you can during a period of 30 minutes, inspect them under the dissecting microscope, and discard or repeat dejelling of those with significant amounts of jelly remaining.

2. Transfer a group of denuded eggs (5-10) in a wide-mouthed pipette to a quartz microscope slide which you have prepared in advance. (Quartz permits passage of UV light while glass does not.) At each end of the slide, place a thin roll of modeling clay. Permit the eggs to rotate so that the vegetal hemispheres are downward, and then remove most of the water from the slide with a Pasteur pipette or some absorbent material. Place a second slide on top of the first. Flatten the eggs between the two slides by exerting firm but gentle pressure on the ends of the upper slide over the modeling clay. This flattening (don't rupture the eggs!) will allow more even irradiation of the hemisphere and will reduce the amount of water intervening between the egg and the slide surface. Water is an effective absorber of UV radiation.

3. All experiments on irradiation of the vegetal pole should be accompanied by parallel control experiments on other eggs in which the animal hemisphere receives an equal dose of radiation. The slides are placed horizontally over (or below) the UV source to irradiate either the vegetal hemisphere (experimental group) or the animal hemisphere (control group). If quartz slides are at a premium, the second slide could be an ordinary glass slide. Of course, in such a case, the animal pole is exposed by placing the quartz slide over the top of the preparation; the bottom slide being an ordinary glass slide.

4. The dosages of UV light received by the eggs will be a function of exposure time and distance from the UV source. Smith (1966) reported that dosages of about 15,000 ergs/mm² of UV light effected depletion of germ cells without causing obviously abnormal development of excessive mortality. Volpe and Curtis (1968) placed the slides at a distance of 18 inches (1 inch = 2.54 cm) directly over a Mineralite (model R-51) ultraviolet lamp. Germ cell formation was completely suppressed when the vegetal hemispheres were exposed to 930 ergs/mm²/min for 45 minutes.

As there are a variety of types of UV sources, conduct several experimental trials with your particular UV source in which the times and distances are varied widely. This is especially important if equipment for measurement of UV output is not available.

5. After irradiation, place the eggs in spring water (or 10% Ringer's solution) and allow them to develop to stage 25 (see Fig. 1-6). At this stage, the primordial germ cells, if present, will appear as light-colored bodies covering the genital ridges. The genital ridges are a pair of longitudinal bands of tissue in the abdominal region along the dorsal body wall, which are clearly evident when the viscera of anesthetized larvae are removed.

B. Analysis of Results

1. Record the protocol of your experiment. Include data on time from fertilization to irradiation for each group of eggs. Record data on stages of developmental arrest in those embryos which die. Are there differences from the patterns which you have previously observed in the total numbers of developmental arrests or stages at which they occur?

2. Prepare a table which includes dosages and results in terms of germ cell numbers. Designations such as "many" ("normal?"), "some," "few," and "none" ("sterile?") would be useful because the exact numbers of germ cells are often difficult to ascertain.

SUGGESTIONS FOR FURTHER INVESTIGATIONS

Smith (1966) reported studies on the relative effectiveness of various wavelengths of light in the UV range in causing reduction in numbers of germ cells. He found that a wavelength of 254 mμ was very effective while the response decreased when light of either shorter (230 mμ) or longer (278 mμ) wavelengths was used. When he transferred vegetal pole subcortical cytoplasm from unirradiated to irradiated eggs, the irradiated embryos developed with gonads containing primordial germ cells. Smith also tested the effects of irradiating eggs at various stages of development, and he found that the optimum effect was obtained when eggs were treated just before or during the first cleavage. He found that the effectiveness of the treatment dropped markedly by the time of the third cleavage and that treatment at the blastula stage had no effect on the ultimate germ cell number. You might enjoy reading his paper and thinking about the developmental significance of these results.

Volpe and Curtis (1968) joined tail-bud stage (stage 17) frog embryos at the gill region in parabiotic unions to examine the possibility of vascular transfer of germ cells between parabionts. In unions of vegetal pole-irradiated embryos with unirradiated embryos, the irradiated member of the pair invariably lacked germ cells (Fig. 5-1). These results provide evidence against the migration of frog primordial germ cells via the vascular route. These experiments might be extended by examining parabiotic unions involving fusions of other areas of the body surface (see Rugh, 1962).

Experiments by Blackler on *Xenopus laevis*, the South African clawed frog, have provided evidence that primordial germ cells give rise to all gametes which ultimately develop in the gonad (Blackler, 1962). This counters the view that some gametes may not be descendants of the primordial germ cells. Blackler (1965) has also demonstrated that primordial germ cells develop in harmony with the gonad which they colonize and differentiate into the type of gamete characteristic of that gonad (*i.e.*, egg or sperm) regardless of their own genetic constitution. You should find the techniques which Blackler employed in these experiments interesting (see also Barth, 1964).

If the total amount of "germinal plasm" in an egg is restricted, what kind of germ cell populations might gonads contain if blastomeres could be separated at the 2-cell stage and allowed to develop separately into 2 tadpoles?

For information on the origin and migration of primordial germ cells in chick embryos, consult the "Suggestions" section of Exercise 9.

REFERENCES

GENERAL

BARTH, L. J. 1964. *Development: selected topics.* Reading, Massachusetts: Addison-Wesley.

HAMBURGER, V. 1960. *A manual of experimental embryology.* Chicago: University of Chicago Press.

RUGH, R. 1962. *Experimental embryology* 3rd ed. Minneapolis: Burgess.

SPECIFIC

BLACKLER, A. W. 1958. Contribution to the study of the germ-cells in Anura. *Jour. Embryol. Exp. Morph.* 6:491-503.

———. 1962. Transfer of primordial germ-cells between two subspecies of *Xenopus laevis. Jour. Embryol. Exp. Morph.* 10:641-651.

———. 1965. Germ-cell transfer and sex ratio in *Xenopus laevis. Jour. Embryol. Exp. Morph.* 13:51-61.

BOUNOURE, L. 1934. Recherches sur la lignée germinale chez la grenouille rousse aux premiers stades du développement. *Ann. Sci. Nat.* 10ᵉ Ser. 17:67-248.

SMITH, L. D. 1966. The role of germinal plasm in the formation of primordial germ cells in *Rana pipiens. Develop. Biol.* 14:330-347.

VOLPE, E. P., and CURTIS, S. 1968. Germ cell chimerism: absence in parabiotic frogs. *Science* 160:328-329.

MATERIALS

EQUIPMENT

Wooden-handle probe (dissecting needle) for pithing

Scissors and forceps for dissection

Disposable Pasteur pipettes or other clean pipettes or medicine droppers

Petri plates

Clean scalpel or section lifter

Watchmaker's forceps

Four-inch fingerbowls or other containers for developing eggs (see Appendix A)

"Frog pipettes"

Quartz microscope slides

Clean glass microscope slides

Binocular dissecting microscope

Illuminator

UV-light source

SOLUTIONS AND CHEMICALS

Spring water or 10% Amphibian Ringer's solution (Appendix A)

Modeling clay

Ethyl m-aminobenzoate methanesulfonate solution (1:3000 in spring water or 10 % Amphibian Ringer's solution)

LIVING MATERIAL

Pituitary-injected female *Rana pipiens*

Male *Rana pipiens*

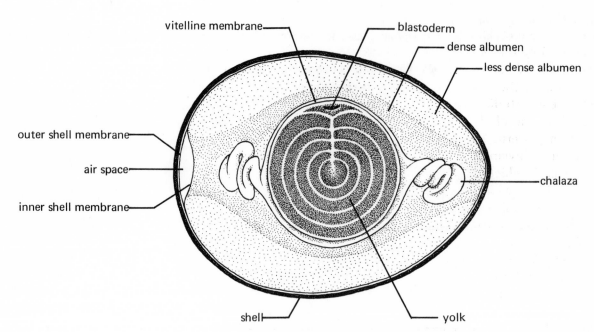

Figure 6-1. The organization of the hen's egg.

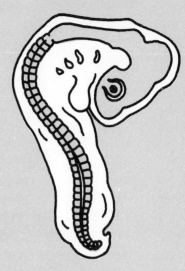

Patterns of Chick Development

The study of the chick embryo has a long history which reaches back to the time of Aristotle and includes such great names in the history of science as Harvey, Wolff, and many others. In modern times, the chick embryo has been exploited in so many developmental studies that it can safely be said that the developing chick is one of the most intensively studied of all organisms. Interest in patterns of chick development goes beyond the basic description of avian ontogeny because there are marked parallels between early chick development and the development of mammalian embryos which are more difficult to obtain and study. This exercise is intended to introduce you to the general processes of chick development and to some of the techniques used in the study of chick embryos.

Many of the early events in chick ontogeny are not as readily observed as are similar processes in the frog. One reason for this difficulty is the organization of the chicken's "egg." The *egg* proper (the "yolk" in everyday terminology) is surrounded by secretory products of the female reproductive tract which include the *white* or *albumen,* the *shell membranes,* and the *shell* (Fig. 6-1). All of these accessory layers are added after the time of fertilization. The egg itself is a large, extremely yolky cell with a restricted cytoplasmic area on one side which contains the nucleus. As the large mass of yolk is not cleaved, the mitotic divisions of cleavage are restricted to the small active area, the *blastodisc.* As cleavage proceeds, the blastodisc is converted into a multicellular structure which is several cells thick. Further development proceeds within this active area which comes to be called the *blastoderm* after cleavage divisions have made it multicellular.

You will begin your study of chick development by removing a blastoderm from the yolk and examining a living chick embryo at an early stage of development. The stage which you will examine is the one made famous by commercially prepared "33-hour chick" slides. This embryo clearly displays many results of the completion

77

Figure 6-2. Opening the incubated hen's egg into saline.

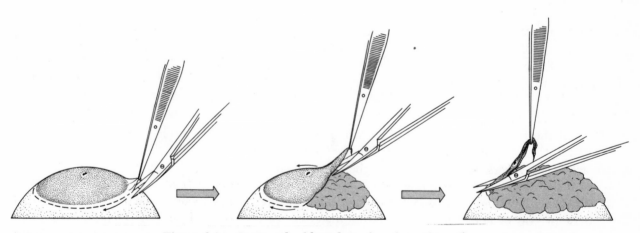

Figure 6-3. Cutting the blastoderm free from the yolk.

of early developmental processes. Following this introduction to the living 12- to 15-somite embryo, we will return to earlier stages of development and trace some general patterns of chick development.

OBSERVATIONS

A. The Living 12- to 15-Somite (33-Hour) Chick Embryo

The length of incubation time required to provide embryos of this stage is somewhat variable and depends upon such factors as the previous handling of the eggs, incubation temperature, and possibly even upon the season of the year. It usually takes more than 33 hours of incubation in modern incubators to carry development to this stage. Thus, it is more accurate to describe the developmental stage of this or any other embryo in terms of a recognized standard such as the Hamburger-Hamilton stages or of a clear morphological criterion such as *somite number*.

1. Pour sterile saline solution into a finger bowl to a depth of about 1.5 cm. Crack the incubated egg out into the saline (Fig. 6-2). It is sometimes helpful to crack the egg gently around at least half of its circumference before attempting to open it. Hold it down near the saline as pressure is applied to separate the two halves. If the yolk breaks, discard the egg and saline and start over with a new egg. The blastoderm usually will be in view when the egg has been broken into the bowl, but it may be necessary to turn this yolk gently using a section lifter, spatula, forceps handle, or some other flat object. The blastoderm area appears to consist of a series of irregular concentric rings. If there is a single, small, dense, white spot, the egg is probably sterile and ought to be discarded, but be cautious about discarding eggs until you are relatively certain about them. Even in the case of a normal blastoderm, the immediate response of students frequently is that, "I can't see a thing." If the blastoderm area of yolk protrudes above the level of the saline, add enough saline to submerge the blastoderm.

2. Firmly grasp the area just outside the blastoderm with watchmaker's forceps. Penetrate the yolk about 0.5 cm before closing the forceps. Hold the forceps closed as you begin to cut around the outside of the blastoderm with a sharp scissors (Fig. 6-3). This cutting of the blastoderm and the *vitelline membrane* which covers it should be done with a fairly rapid snipping action. You will encounter problems caused by yolk rushing out of the first cuts unless the blastoderm is held in place at the very top of the yolk. After you have cut around the entire blastoderm, the vitelline membrane and blastoderm area can be gently peeled back off the yolk into the saline. Some yolk will adhere to the blastoderm and it may be necessary to break the continuity of this yolk with the remainder of the yolk being left behind by cutting into the yolk repeatedly with your scissors.

When the blastoderm, with a small amount of adherent yolk, is floated free, it can be transferred in a wide-mouth "chick" pipette to a Syracuse dish which is about 2/3 full of saline. Several difficulties can be encountered in this step. Since the blastoderm and vitelline membrane tend to stick to the inside of the pipette unless it is completely wetted, it is necessary to flush the pipette several times by repeatedly drawing saline in and out. Another problem is the tendency of stringy albumen to remain attached to the vitelline membrane and to pull the membrane and the blastoderm back out of the pipette during the transfer. This can cause damage to the blastoderm and is a source of considerable frustration. This stringy albumen either can be cut with a scissors or pinched off with a forceps. Sometimes, however, the only effective technique is to hold the flat handle of the forceps over the mouth of the pipette during the transfer process. It is also helpful to hold the pipette as close to horizontal as possible and to make the transfer quickly because there is a natural tendency for everything to run out of such a wide opening. *Gently* expel the contents into saline in a Syracuse dish.

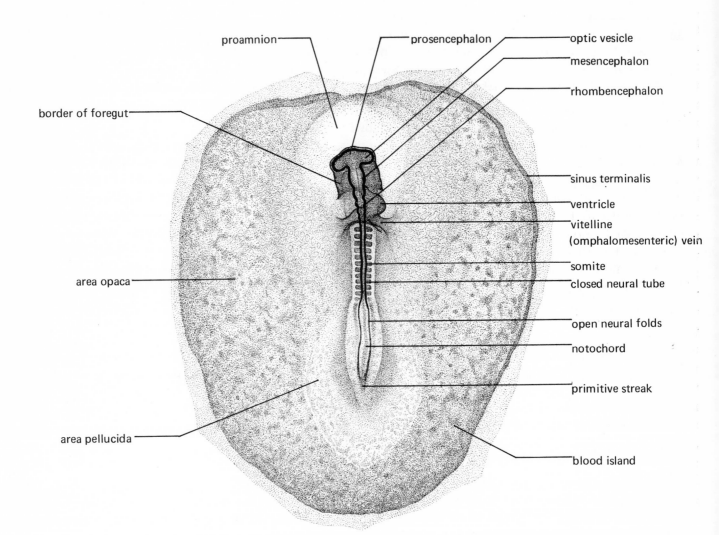

proamnion — prosencephalon — optic vesicle

mesencephalon

rhombencephalon

border of foregut

sinus terminalis

ventricle

vitelline (omphalomesenteric) vein

somite

closed neural tube

area opaca

open neural folds

notochord

primitive streak

area pellucida

blood island

Figure 6-4. Dorsal view of a 14- or 15-somite chick embryo.

3. Further work should be done under a dissecting microscope, and it is frequently helpful to switch from a light to a dark background and back again. A dark background can be provided by either the dark side of the stage plate if your microscope has one or by a piece of black paper placed on the stage. The blastoderm still may be covered by the vitelline membrane. If it is lying with the vitelline membrane on top, you will need to turn it over gently. When you have the blastoderm side exposed, quickly remove the largest yolk granules by picking them off with your forceps or by squirting a gentle stream of saline from a Pasteur pipette. If the vitelline membrane still is attached, free the blastoderm by teasing it loose around the edges. If this is done carefully, the blastoderm should survive the procedure without injury. It probably will be necessary to transfer the blastoderm to a second Syracuse dish with clean saline before further observations can be made. Be very careful during this final transfer of the fragile, unprotected blastoderm and make certain that the inside of your "chick" pipette is thoroughly pre-wetted.

4. Examine, sketch, and/or describe dorsal and ventral views of the 12- to 15-somite chick embryo using Figure 6-4 for reference. It is difficult to locate some of the structures represented in Figure 6-4 with certainty in the living embryo, but there are a number of general structural features which we will call specifically to your attention in the following sections. Identify the *somites* which are paired, compact chunks of mesodermal tissue which occur lateral to the neural tube. With your embryo against a dark background, count the number of pairs of somites. If your embryo has less than 10 pairs or more than 17 pairs of somites, it may be difficult to follow these descriptions and you should ask your instructor whether you ought to try another embryo.

5. You will note that there are differences in the apparent consistency of the blastoderm surrounding the body of the embryo proper. The relatively clear area adjacent to the embryo (*area pellucida*) along with the embryo itself is separated from the yolk by a fluid-filled space when it is in place in the egg. The remainder of the blastoderm (*area opaca*) is situated in closer contact with the yolk and its cells carry yolk granules giving it a more opaque appearance.

6. During your examination of the *dorsal view* of the blastoderm, gently poke the embryo with a tungsten needle, a probe, or a forceps tip in order to clarify its structural dimensions. Note that the embryo has a definite head region which is a clearly delineated tubular structure. The head end of the embryo has, thus, been segregated from the remainder of the blastoderm. In the more posterior areas you will note continuity of the still-flat posterior part of the embryo with the remainder of the flat blastoderm. The progressive segregation of the originally flat and continuous blastoderm into a rounded embryonic body area and an *extra-embryonic* area is accomplished by complicated processes known as *body folding*. The necessity for this process arises, of course, from the fact that in early development the large, yolky egg cell is not divided completely as cleavage is restricted to the flat disc of active cytoplasm on one side of the egg.

7. Examine the embryo against a light background and look for scattered reddish or orange spots, the *blood islands*. These blood islands are early sites of blood cell production and are in the process of fusing to produce blood vessels at this stage. You also may be able to see some color in the *sinus terminalis* which is a ring-like vessel encircling the margin of the area of the blastoderm which contains developing blood vessels. The cellular blastoderm does extend beyond the sinus terminalis. Thus, the sinus does not mark the margin of the blastoderm.

8. While examining the *ventral surface* of the embryo, observe the *heart* and the large vessels (*vitelline or omphalomesenteric veins*) which enter it posteriorly. You may observe heart pulsation, but it probably will be irregular.

Note that there is an enclosed hollow gut (*foregut*) in the anterior part of the embryo which is open posteriorly (Fig. 6-5). This posterior opening to the outside is known as the *intestinal portal*. The foregut at this stage has been described as resembling the finger of a glove. Probe the gut to demonstrate its dimensions to your own satisfaction.

9. You may supplement your study of the 12- to 15-somite embryo by examining a commercially-prepared, stained slide of an embryo at this stage of development (*i.e.*, a "33-hour chick" slide).

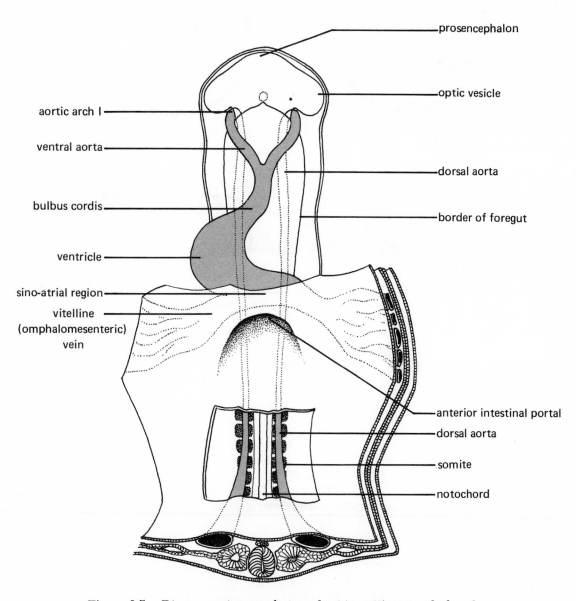

Figure 6-5. Diagrammatic ventral view of a 14- or 15-somite chick embryo.

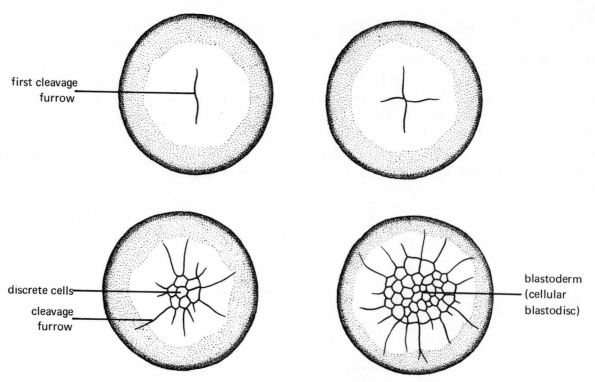

first cleavage furrow

discrete cells

cleavage furrow

blastoderm (cellular blastodisc)

Figure 6-6. Surface views of cleavage of the avian blastodisc.

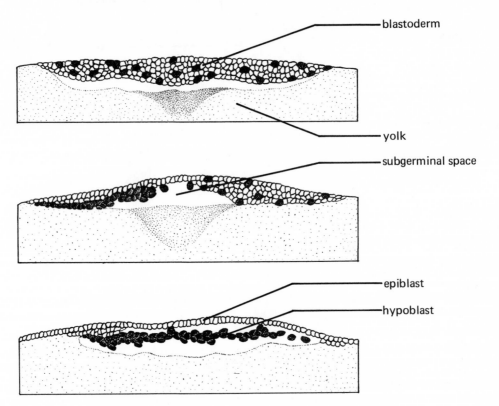

blastoderm

yolk

subgerminal space

epiblast

hypoblast

Figure 6-7. Diagrammatic representation of the separation of hyboblast and epiblast (delamination) in the avian blastoderm. (These sections of blastoderms are more advanced than the blastoderms shown in Fig. 6-6).

B. Cleavage in the Chick Embryo

Now that you have had opportunity to examine an embryo at the end of the early phases of development, we will return to the initial steps of chick development and retrace some of the processes which produced the embryo which you have studied.

Fertilization occurs in the upper portion of the hen's oviduct and cleavage begins. The early processes to be described here occur as the egg passes through the hen's *oviduct* and *shell gland* (*uterus*), and it is quite difficult to obtain embryos at these stages and to prepare them for study. Therefore, we simply will describe some of the highlights of development before the time of egg laying without asking you to make direct observations.

The mitotic divisions of *cleavage* proceed as the egg moves through the oviduct. Cleavage in the chick is called *partial* or *discoidal* because the huge mass of yolk does not divide into separate cells, and the cleavage divisions are restricted to the active cytoplasmic area, the *blastodisc*. Early nuclear duplication and division is not followed by complete cytoplasmic division. Initially, the nuclei are segregated by furrows in the blastodisc (Fig. 6-6). As further nuclear divisions occur, and the furrowing process spreads peripherally from the center of the blastoderm, segregation of some discrete cells is completed at the center of the blastodisc (properly called *blastoderm* henceforth). As cleavage continues, the blastoderm comes to be several cells in thickness, and a fluid filled *sub-germinal space* develops underneath it.

C. Gastrulation and Neurulation

The beginning of *gastrulation,* the process which ultimately produces the major body layers (*germ layers*), also occurs during passage through the hen's reproductive tract. Some of the cells of the blastoderm separate themselves from the remainder of the blastoderm and move down toward the subgerminal space (Fig. 6-7). This segregation process occurs through the action of individual cells or small clusters of cells. The end result is the production of two layers separated by a space. These layers are the newly formed lower layer or *hypoblast* which is rather diffuse and loosely organized and the upper layer or *epiblast* within which the cells are arranged in an orderly epithelial type of organization. This process of separation into two layers is known as *delamination.* The developmental fate of the hypoblast will be the production of *extra-embryonic endoderm* of the *yolk sac* membrane. Following delamination, cells of the epiblast move to new positions in the embryo where they will participate in the development of many structures. The developmental roles of the cells in various areas of the original epiblast can be summarized in the form of a *fate map* such as Figure 6-8.

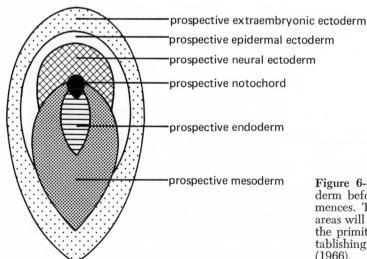

prospective extraembryonic ectoderm

prospective epidermal ectoderm

prospective neural ectoderm

prospective notochord

prospective endoderm

prospective mesoderm

Figure 6-8. Fate map of the epiblast of the chick blastoderm before migration through the primitive streak commences. The future notochord, mesoderm, and endoderm areas will leave the surface and pass to the interior through the primitive streak. For details of techniques used in establishing the areas of the fate map, consult Rosenquist (1966).

85

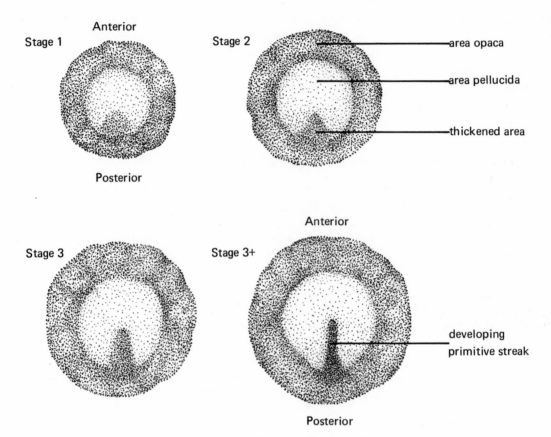

Figure 6-9. Stages in the formation of the primitive streak (Hamburger-Hamilton stages 1, 2, 3, 3+).

At the time that the egg is laid, delamination is arrested and is resumed only if the egg is brought to incubation temperatures. When incubation is initiated, delamination continues, and other organizational changes occur in the blastoderm. A markedly thickened area develops on one side of the blastoderm (Fig. 6-9). This thickening is the beginning of the formation of the site of cellular migration which will occur during later stages of gastrulation. This area, the *primitive streak*, elongates as incubation proceeds.

When active cell migration begins in the primitive streak, cells of the epiblast layer move toward, down into, and away from the primitive streak. Thus, they move across the surface to congregate at the primitive streak, leave the surface to move down in the direction of the subgerminal space, and then change direction to move out away from the streak to take their places as the mesodermal layer and the embryonic portion of the endoderm (Fig. 6-10).

1. As migration through the streak continues, several structural features of the fully-developed or *definitive primitive streak* can be identified (Fig. 6-10). The midline of the streak becomes depressed. This shallow trough, the *primitive groove*, lies between paired *primitive ridges*. At the anterior end of the streak there is a particularly marked accumulation of migrating cells, *Hensen's node*. Just posterior to this enlargement the midline portion streak is deeply depressed to form the *primitive pit*.

A.

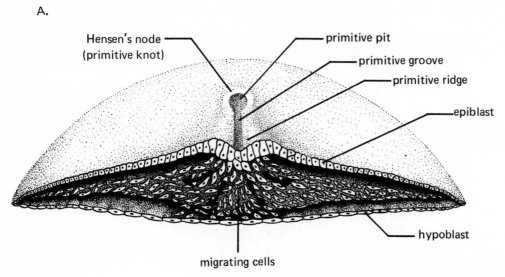

Figure 6-10. The mechanics of gastrulation in the chick embryo. A. Diagrammatic cross section of the blastoderm showing the migration of epiblast cells through the primitive streak to produce mesoderm and embryonic endoderm. (Adapted from Balinsky: *An Introduction to Embryology*, 3rd edition, 1970, with permission of W. B. Saunders Co.) B. Diagrammatic longitudinal section of the primitive streak showing the migration of cells which produce the notochord.

B.

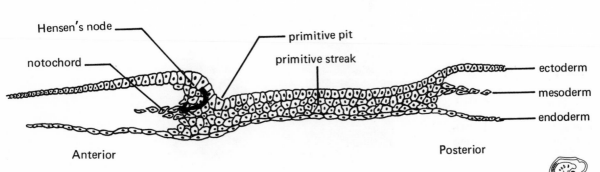

87

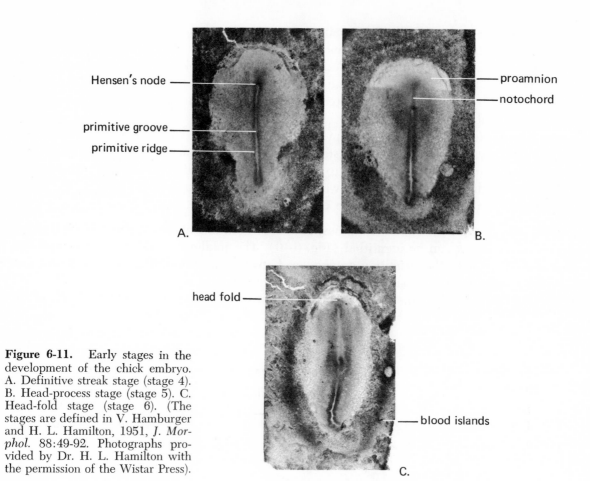

Hensen's node —

primitive groove —

primitive ridge —

A.

— proamnion

— notochord

B.

head fold —

— blood islands

C.

Figure 6-11. Early stages in the development of the chick embryo. A. Definitive streak stage (stage 4). B. Head-process stage (stage 5). C. Head-fold stage (stage 6). (The stages are defined in V. Hamburger and H. L. Hamilton, 1951, *J. Morphol.* 88:49-92. Photographs provided by Dr. H. L. Hamilton with the permission of the Wistar Press).

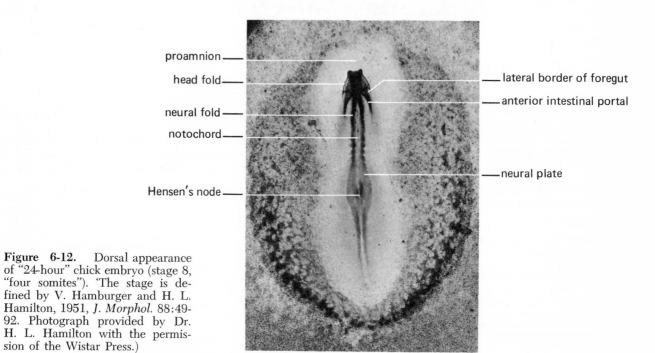

proamnion —

head fold —

neural fold —

notochord —

Hensen's node —

— lateral border of foregut

— anterior intestinal portal

— neural plate

Figure 6-12. Dorsal appearance of "24-hour" chick embryo (stage 8, "four somites"). The stage is defined by V. Hamburger and H. L. Hamilton, 1951, *J. Morphol.* 88:49-92. Photograph provided by Dr. H. L. Hamilton with the permission of the Wistar Press.)

Examine a commercially prepared whole-mount slide of a definitive primitive streak stage (H.-H. stage 4, 12- to 16-hours incubation time) chick blastoderm and identify the areas of the streak and other features of the embryo (see Fig. 6-11).

2. During early stages of migration through the primitive streak, the cells of the intermediate or mesodermal layer spread laterally and posteriorly from the streak in the form of sheets of cells. Migration of mesoderm in an anterior direction from the streak begins with a cord of cells which has moved through the primitive pit region. This cord of cells produces the mid-dorsal supporting element known as the *notochord* or *head process* (Figs. 6-10, 6-11). As the notochord develops, the primitive streak begins to regress. The anterior end of the streak retreats causing a shortening in the length of the streak. The shortening streak leaves behind the lengthening notochord which almost appears to be reeled out by the retreating tip of the primitive streak (Fig. 6-11).

Examine a commercial whole-mount slide of an 18-hour chick blastoderm. It may be necessary to examine several slides of this stage of development and to focus up and down on the slides in order to satisfy yourself that you have actually seen the notochord and other features of the blastoderm at this stage.

3. Before the completion of gastrulation, other developmental events are already under way. The formation of the central nervous system, *neurulation,* begins with the formation of a thickened area of ectoderm lying over the region of the notochord. This thickened *neural plate* rolls up into the cylindrical *neural tube* by processes which are roughly similar to those seen in the frog embryo. We will examine details of neural tube formation later. At the same time that the neural tube is forming, mesoderm paralleling the midline of the embryo initiates organization of the paired, segmentally arranged somites. As mentioned earlier, somite number is a much more reliable standard for communication of developmental stage than is incubation time because development of additional pairs of somites is closely related to general level of ontogeny of the whole embryo. The first evidence of the body folding process which segregates the embryo proper from the remainder of the blastoderm can also be seen at about the same time. In some cases, the *head fold* has undercut embryos of this stage of incubation to establish the embryo's head (Fig. 6-12).

Examine a commercial "24-hour" embryo slide and identify as many of these features as possible. Prepare a living blastoderm of 28-30 hours incubation for study using the techniques employed in section A. Identify the major landmarks of the embryo once again and then proceed to investigate the 3-dimensional structure of the embryo. Probe the head region from the dorsal side and the foregut from the ventral side in order to clarify the nature and results of the process of head folding. Your instructor may request that you examine sections of the 24-hour embryo or other slide material to amplify the general outline of early development which we have considered. Whether or not you make further observations on early stages of chick development, we urge you to expand your understanding of early chick development by filling in details from your text and from the references listed at the end of this exercise.

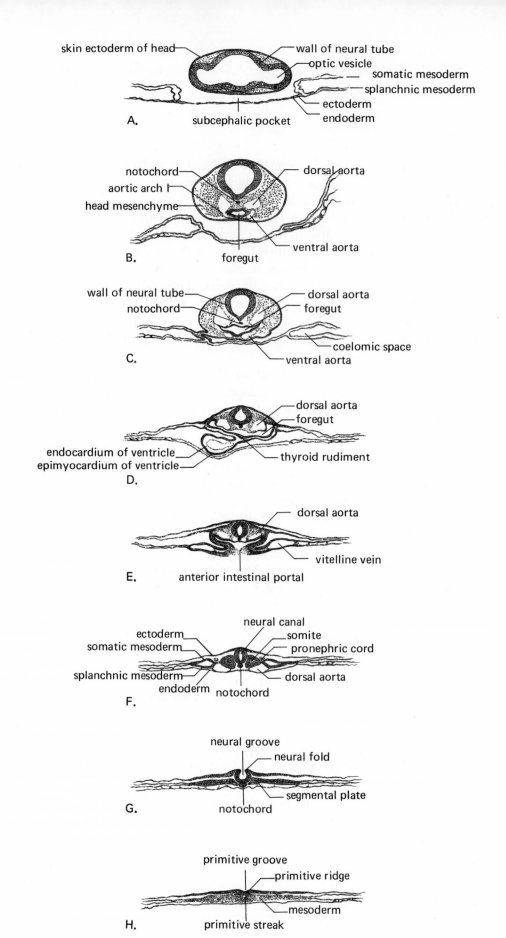

Figure 6-13. Representative cross-sections of a 12- to 15-somite chick embryo.

D. Structural Details of the 12- to 15-Somite Stage Chick Embryo

Now that you have surveyed some basic events in early development and have a general grasp of some of the processes which lead to the formation of the "33-hour" chick, we will return to that stage of development for a somewhat more detailed study. The relationships of the various body layers to one another and their differentiation into specific structural elements of the embryo can be reconstructed through the study of serial sections of the embryo.

1. In order to put your study of serial sections in perspective, reexamine a commercially prepared "33-hour" chick whole mount slide before you begin to examine serial sections. Note again such features as the differentiation of various areas of the neural tube, the structure and location of the heart, and the apparent extent of progress of the anterior body fold in freeing the head from the flat blastoderm. Consult Figures 6-4 and 6-5.

2. Begin your study by skimming rather quickly through all of the sections from the anterior tip of the embryo through the last section. You will notice that the embryo apparently is free in the first sections that you encountered, and that it is separated from the remainder of the blastoderm by a definite space, the *subcephalic pocket* (Fig. 6-13A). As you proceed further through the sections, you will reach sections where the embryo is no longer physically separated from the remainder of the flat blastoderm. The point where this continuity is first encountered is the end of the free portion of the embryo produced by the body folds up to this time. Move on through the remainder of the slides noting the continuity of the embryo with the rest of the flat blastoderm and the general shape changes seen in embryonic structures at various levels of the body as you move posteriorly.

3. Return to the first sections of the head and trace the neural tube posteriorly through the body. Within a few sections the neural tube will broaden laterally (Fig. 6-13A). These lateral extensions are the *optic vesicles* which will produce major portions of the eyes. As you move further posteriorly, the neural tube changes in shape and size as the optic vesicles fade out and various other regions of the brain are sectioned. Ultimately the future *spinal cord* level of the neural tube is reached. Sections of the neural tube in the spinal cord region are characterized by a narrow, tall, sometimes slit-like, central cavity and a laterally-compressed shape. Note also that the floor and roof of the spinal cord are relatively thin compared to the lateral walls. As you continue tracing sections, you will move into the region where the neural tube has not yet closed. In this region you can identify the *open neural groove* and the paired *neural folds* (Fig. 6-13G). By moving back and forth through the region of transition from closed to open neural tube you should be able to mentally reconstruct the process of neural tube closure. You may wish to make sketches of your notion of neural tube closure and later compare them with those in textbooks.

4. During your examination of the neural tube, you undoubtedly will have noticed the circular *notochord* which lies just ventral to the neural tube. Quickly trace the notochord through its entire extent. Note that it does not extend all the way to the tip of the head, but rather is first encountered just posterior to the point where the optic vesicles fade out. Near its posterior end, sections of the notochord enlarge and eventually the notochord fuses with the floor of the open neural plate. As you progress beyond this point, you are entering the area of the *primitive streak*. It is somewhat difficult to give an exact description of guidelines which indicate that you have reached sections of the streak, but Figure 6-13H is a representative section of the primitive streak level of the embryo.

5. The *foregut* (Fig. 6-13B) appears in serial sections just posterior to the level at which the optic vesicles fade out. Trace the foregut posteriorly. You will note that it becomes laterally expanded, and that it appears to be quite flattened dorso-ventrally. However, remember that in your study of the living embryo at this stage, it was possible to insert a relatively large object such

91

as the tip of a tungsten needle through the intestinal portal into the foregut. Continue tracing the foregut until the floor of the gut appears to pull apart within a span of three or four sections. You have now reached the level of the *anterior intestinal portal* (Fig. 6-13E). You should now be able to reconstruct the significance of these sections mentally if you think back to the organization of the living embryo, the structure of the foregut, and the process of body folding which is progressively defining the embryonic body at this stage of development. Posterior to the level of the intestinal portal, the prospective endodermal lining of the remainder of the digestive tract is continuous with the more lateral future yolk sac endoderm. This region of flat endoderm is called the *open gut*.

Later in development, body folding will begin at the posterior end of the embryo and will produce a *hindgut* and a *posterior intestinal portal*. Then lateral body folding will progress from both directions adding to the extent of the foregut and hindgut as well as defining more of the embryonic body. Ultimately this process reduces the area of the embryo in continuity with the remainder of the blastoderm to the very small *umbilical region* which includes a small area of open gut. This small persisting area of continuity provides the embryo's contact with the extraembryonic membranes and a pathway for blood vessels to and from the membranes and will be maintained until just before the time of hatching.

6. Figures 6-4 and 6-5 illustrate the general organization of the major portions of the circulatory system of the embryo. Return to the level at which the foregut first appears in your sections and in that section or 1 or 2 sections anterior to it note a space on either side of the region of the tip of the gut. These are sections through the first pair of *aortic arches* (Fig. 6-13B, see also Fig. 6-5) which loop up around the front of the foregut. Posterior to this point, the laterally-expanded gut lies between the paired *ventral aortae* carrying blood ahead from the heart and the paired *dorsal aortae* carrying blood back toward the posterior areas of the embryo. Later in development, posterior portions of the dorsal aortae will fuse into a single large arterial trunk.

Trace sections posteriorly and watch both ventral and dorsal aortae. The ventral aortae appear to fuse into a single vessel. This is actually a section through the anterior end of the heart, the *bulbus cordis*. As you proceed posteriorly, the heart will appear to move to the side from its original position beneath the midline of the embryo. This laterally deflected portion of the heart is the developing *ventricle*. In subsequent sections as you continue posteriorly the heart appears to return to the midline and then to split in two portions. This single midline region and the first portions of the paired vessels represent the *sinoatrial* portion of the heart which will produce the *atrium* and *sinus venosus* regions.

These paired vessels continue posteriorly, without any marked boundary, as the *vitelline* or *omphalomesenteric veins* (Fig. 6-13E). These veins drain blood from the developing yolk sac region and return it to the heart. Note the relationship of the vitelline veins to the intestinal portal in your sections (See also Fig. 6-5). As you continue tracing the vitelline veins posteriorly, they appear to become laterally expanded. This is actually an indication that you have reached the point where the vitelline veins approach the embryo at nearly right angles. All trace of the vitelline veins will soon be lost in succeeding sections.

Continue following the dorsal aortae through the sections. Note that there are apparent lateral expansions of the aorta in the posterior region of the body, and that ultimately the aortae disappear from the sections. These lateral expansions represent the origins of the *vitelline arteries* which supply the developing yolk sac region.

It might be helpful for your understanding of the circulatory pattern to sketch a complete circulatory system with arrows indicating the directions of blood flow. Your instructor may also ask you to read about earlier stages of development of the single tubular heart from paired rudiments (see suggestions section).

93

7. Choose a section in the spinal cord region of the body which has well-developed somites (Fig. 6-13F) and study the general relationships of the various body structures and layers to one another. This type of section displays a number of characteristic features of a general body organization pattern which is a recognizable stage in the development of all vertebrate embryos. However, remember that at this stage of chick development the body layers (*germ layers*) are still stacked on top of one another on a flat plane in this area of the embryo. We would suggest that you sketch this section and add details as your study proceeds. The presence of a hollow neural tube and a rod-like notochord just ventral to it are obvious features which need little further mention, but we will examine some other features of this characteristic vertebrate embryonic body plan in more detail. The upper ectodermal and lower endodermal layers are relatively simply organized, but there are regional specializations in the mesoderm which are important characteristics of this basic body plan. We will concentrate on lateral aspects of the mesoderm after simply asking you to recall the method of formation and structural relationships of the mesodermal notochord.

Focus your attention on the somites and scan back and forth through eight or ten sections in this part of the body. Note that the somites appear to be dense and compact in some sections and rather diffuse and loosely organized in other sections. These sections showing apparently diffuse organization are actually cut through the spaces between the somites while the dense, compact areas are sections through the somites themselves. These observations should serve as a reinforcement of your understanding of the somites as paired, segmentally arranged blocks of mesodermal tissue.

Shift your attention laterally from the somite. Just beyond the somite there is a solid strip of tissue which is known as the *nephrotome*. This is the portion of the mesoderm from which excretory and reproductive structures will develop. In fact, you may be able to distinguish the very first elements of the developing excretory system, the *pronephric cords*, in some sections in the area of the embryo under examination (See Fig. 6-13F).

The portion of the mesoderm beyond the nephrotome is known as the *lateral plate*. The lateral plate mesoderm is split into two layers. The lower of these, the *splanchnic mesodermal* layer, lies adjacent to the endoderm while the other, the *somatic mesodermal* layer, lies adjacent to the ectoderm. The space betwen these layers is the *coelomic space*.

8. We would like to suggest one further exercise to aid your understanding of the organization of the basic body plan of this stage of development. Figure 2-7E is a cross section of the trunk of a frog embryo which possesses the same basic structural features that you have observed in the chick embryo. Diagrammatically alter a sketch of this chick embryo section to make it resemble the tubular body of the 3-mm frog embryo. The significance of this exercise in diagrammatic modification of a chick embryo section goes beyond simply facilitating your comparison of body organizations in the tubular frog embryo and the still-flat chick blastoderm. The structural modifications which you have performed on the chick cross section in this sketch are very similar to the changes brought about by the process of *body folding* which segregates the embryonic portion of the blastoderm and produces the tubular body form of the advanced chick embryo.

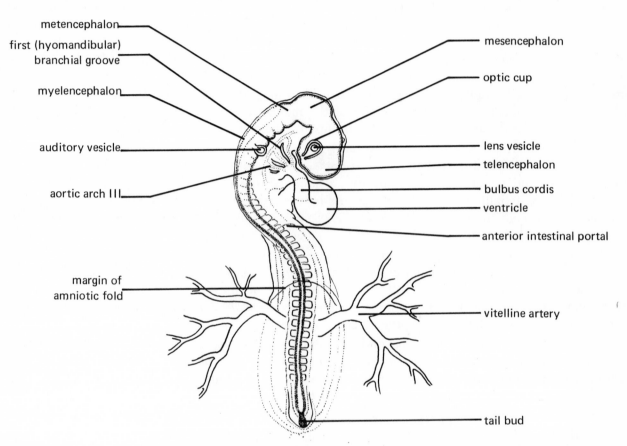

metencephalon

first (hyomandibular) branchial groove

myelencephalon

auditory vesicle

aortic arch III

margin of amniotic fold

mesencephalon

optic cup

lens vesicle

telencephalon

bulbus cordis

ventricle

anterior intestinal portal

vitelline artery

tail bud

Figure 6-14. Outline drawing of a 29-somite chick embryo (after slightly more than two days of incubation).

E. The Chick Embryo After Two Days of Incubation

Our relatively detailed study of the "33-hour" embryo should have given you a picture of the internal organization of the chick embryo at the end of the early phases of its development. We will now turn our attention to later stages of development which we will consider in a more general way. Our goal is to gain an overview of successive stages in chick development, and we will emphasize those points which will be helpful in your later experimental work. Your instructor may elect to ask you to go into more detail than that offered in the descriptions that follow. If this is the case, consult references cited in the General Reference section.

1. Figure 6-14 will provide you with guidance for a preliminary examination of a commercial "48-hour" chick embryo. This embryo is at a stage of development roughly comparable to that of the living 2-day embryo which you will examine.

Your instructor will specify the amount of detail required in examination of brain, circulatory system, pharynx, and other parts of the embryo on the prepared slide, but there are some general points which we wish to make. Note the orientation of the embryo's head which is no longer a simple tubular structure as it was in the 12- to 15-somite chick. The head has been tipped forward in a process known as *flexion*. At the same time the body has begun to twist on its axis in such a way that the anterior portion of the head has come to lie on its left side. This twisting of the body axis is called *torsion*.

The primitive streak has regressed into a restricted area known as the *tail bud*. The tail bud continues to play a role in organizing the posterior area of the embryo.

Note the rather prominent *vitelline arteries* which extend out at right angles from the posterior part of the embryo. In a prepared slide it is more difficult to see the *vitelline veins* approaching the embryo, but the complex nature of the *yolk sac* circulation will be obvious in the living embryo.

Finally, note the margin of the *amniotic fold* which is in the process of covering the embryo. The amniotic fold produces the *amnion* which will come to surround and enclose the embryo and the *chorion* which will spread peripherally around the whole complex of embryo and yolk. We will examine some details of amnion production later.

2. The living 2-day embryo can be observed on the surface of the yolk. Break an incubated egg into saline in a finger bowl. Crack the egg gently for quite a distance around its circumference and partially submerge it in the saline as you pull the 2 halves apart. Even if you observe these precautions carefully, it is quite possible that you will break the yolk because its consistency is beginning to change at this stage and yolk breakage is a greater hazard now than at earlier stages. If you break the yolk, try again. If the blastoderm is not covered, add enough saline to submerge it completely. When the yolk is in the saline, the embryo and the yolk sac vessels should be seen readily because the sinus terminalis now completely encircles an area which is several centimeters in diameter. The blastoderm area should rotate upward, but you may have to assist the yolk's rotation gently.

Make observations of the pattern of circulation with the embryo still in place on the yolk. Attempt to determine which major extraembryonic vessels are arteries and which are veins. Focus on the vessels carefully with your dissecting microscope and check the direction and rate of blood flow in the vessels, if possible. Blood will be flowing away from the embryo in arteries and toward it in veins, and flow in arteries shows some surging pulses while the venous flow is smoother and more regular. If you are unable to make all of these observations with the embryo in place on the yolk, do so after you have removed it to a dish.

Examine the heart which has folded on itself to produce a coiled tube and trace the flow of blood through the heart.

97

A.

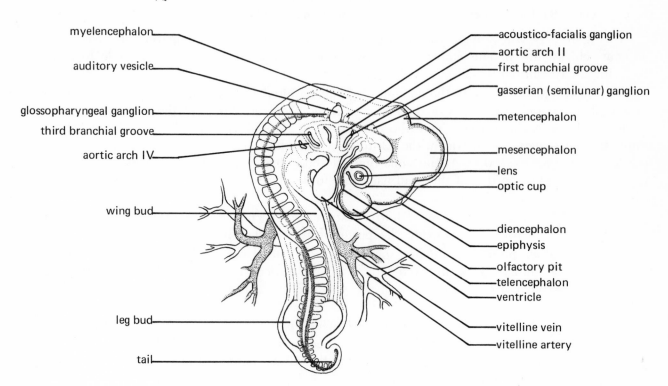

myelencephalon — acoustico-facialis ganglion

auditory vesicle — aortic arch II

first branchial groove

gasserian (semilunar) ganglion

glossopharyngeal ganglion — metencephalon

third branchial groove — mesencephalon

aortic arch IV — lens

optic cup

wing bud

diencephalon

epiphysis

olfactory pit

telencephalon

ventricle

leg bud

vitelline vein

vitelline artery

tail

Figure 6-15. Outline views of a 36-somite chick embryo (after three days of incubation). A. Dorsal view. B. Ventral view emphasizing the connection of the vitelline vessels and the developing allantois. (Adapted from Balinsky: *An Introduction to Embryology*, 3rd edition, 1970, with permission of W. B. Saunders Co.)

B.

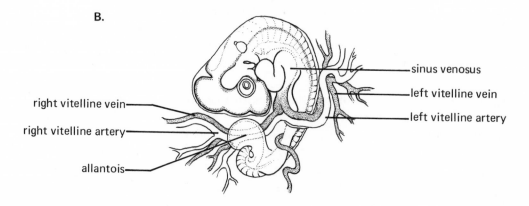

sinus venosus

left vitelline vein

right vitelline vein — left vitelline artery

right vitelline artery

allantois

3. Further observations can be made more easily after the blastoderm has been removed from the yolk. Grasp the blastoderm with your forceps and cut a circle just outside the sinus terminalis. Pull the blastoderm off and transfer it to a dish of saline for observation using the techniques which you have used previously. Very careful pre-wetting of your chick pipette and cautious manipulation of the bulb are essential for a succesful transfer.

You probably will find that the vitelline membrane floats off more easily than it did at earlier stages of development.

4. Examine the dorsal side of the embryo and blastoderm. There are general features which should be examined in addition to structural details of the embryonic body itself. Note that the amniotic folds form a hood-like covering which has moved back over part of the embryo's body. Use a probe or tungsten needle to investigate the nature of this relationship. Ultimately, the amniotic folds will cover the embryo completely. Other features which should be noted are the increased somite number and any aspects of the circulatory pattern which you were unable to observe with the embryo in place on the yolk. All of the extraembryonic vessels observed here are part of the blood supply of the yolk-sac membrane which is spreading peripherally to cover an increasing area of the yolk.

Turn the blastoderm over and examine its ventral surface. Note the restricted area of blood vessel connection between the embryo and the yolk sac. The anterior intestinal portal can still be probed, but the structure of the foregut has been altered considerably by head flexion. Body folding in the posterior part of the embryo may be apparent; and, if so, you should be able to insert an instrument through a *posterior intestinal portal* into the *hindgut*.

5. In order to examine structural details of the embryo, it will be necessary to dissect away the amniotic folds. Note the increased amount of free head. Use Figure 6-14 and reference sources for information for study of the embryo itself.

F. The Chick Embryo After Three Days of Incubation

Our study of the 3-day chick embryo and its relationship to extraembryonic structures will emphasize changing general structural patterns, but your instructor may direct you to do more detailed study in some places.

1. Examine a commercially-prepared "72-hour" chick slide using Figure 6-15A as a guide.

2. Carefully open an incubated egg in a dish of saline. It is hard to avoid breaking the yolk because of the more fluid consistency of the yolk at this stage, but small breaks can sometimes be tolerated.

It is much easier to observe the embryo and the extraembryonic circulation in place on the yolk at three days' incubation than it was in the case of the 2-day embryo. Reaffirm your understanding of the vitelline circulatory pattern. Note that the area enclosed within the sinus terminalis has increased markedly during an additional day of incubation.

3. It usually is not practical to attempt to remove the whole vascular area when transferring the embryo for further study. Therefore, make your encircling cut well inside the sinus terminalis. Transfer of the 3-day embryo and blastoderm with a "chick" pipette should not be attempted. If you hold your Syracuse dish close enough to the finger bowl to avoid a long transfer distance, it is possible to pick up the blastoderm with watchmaker's forceps. An alternative method is to float the blastoderm onto a watch glass and hold it in place as you lift it out of the saline for transfer to your Syracuse dish. The vitelline membrane may be lost in the transfer, but if it is still attached, remove it carefully.

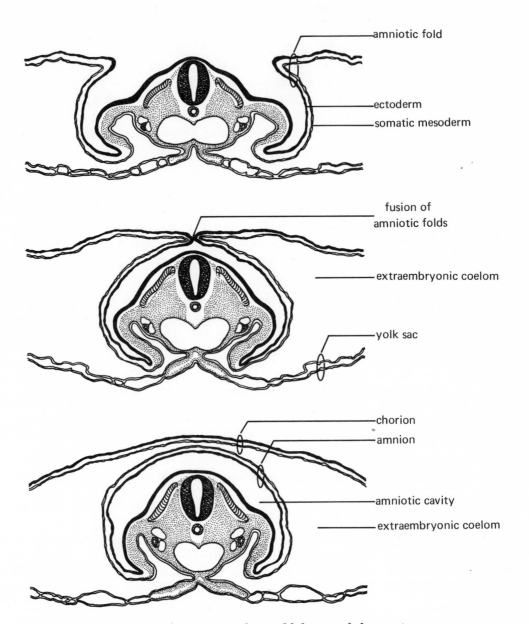

amniotic fold

ectoderm

somatic mesoderm

fusion of
amniotic folds

extraembryonic coelom

yolk sac

chorion

amnion

amniotic cavity

extraembryonic coelom

Figure 6-16. Stages in the establishment of the amnion and the chorion by fusion of the amniotic folds.

4. You will find that the body of the embryo is largely or, possibly, completely covered by the amniotic folds by this stage. If a small circular uncovered area remains over your embryo, note that in addition to the anterior amniotic fold which you observed in the 2-day chick, there is amniotic folding moving in from the rear and the sides of the embryo. These folds come together in a process which some observers have likened to the closing of a drawstring purse. The amniotic folds are produced by a buckling of the extraembryonic ectoderm and the somatic mesoderm adjacent to it. These folds meet over the body of the embryo and fuse (Fig. 6-16). At the point of contact, a separation occurs which leaves two distinct membranes. One is the *amnion* enclosing the *amniotic cavity* within which the embryo continues its development. The other is the *chorion* (*serosa*) which spreads peripherally to enclose the embryo and yolk (see Figure 6-17 also).

5. Before making further observations of the dorsal view of the embryo, turn the blastoderm over and examine the ventral surface. Make certain that the embryo itself is lying on its right side before proceeding. Refer to Figure 6-15B and examine the relationship of the large yolk sac vessels to the embryo. You will see that the area of entry and exit of large veins and arteries is restricted to a small area, the developing *umbilical cord* region.

Note that just anterior to the tail region a round vesicle has grown out ventrally from the body. This hollow sac is the developing *allantois*. The allantois plays several roles later in development. It will serve as a storage depot for excretory wastes produced during the course of development, and it will expand distally, spread, and fuse with the chorion to produce a complex, highly vascular membrane known as the *chorio-allantoic membrane* (see Figure 6-17). This membrane plays a critical role as an area of gas exchange where oxygen diffusing in through the porous shell is absorbed for transport back to the embryo and carbon dioxide is released. The allantois remains attached by a narrow stalk running through the umbilical cord.

6. It will be necessary to dissect away the chorion and amnion in order to examine details of the structure of the embryo itself. (Consult Figure 6-15). You will observe marked changes in the flexion of the head and the differentiation of various regions of the brain. The very clear establishment of a tail region and the development of prominent limb buds are other gross features which mark this stage of development. Increased complexity in heart structure and also in the pharynx and aortic arch region can also be seen.

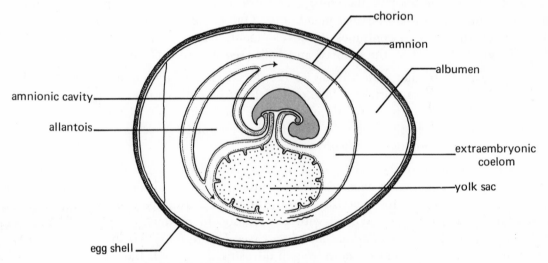

Figure 6-17. Membrane relationships in the chick embryo. (Adapted from Balinsky: *An Introduction to Embryology,* 3rd edition, 1970, with permission of W. B. Saunders Co.)

G. Later Stages of Chick Development

1. Examine a series of chick embryos which have been incubated for a longer period of time. We would suggest a series which includes embryos of 5, 7 or 8, 10, and 17 or 18 days' incubation. Your instructor may elect to eliminate some stages or to substitute others. The best technique for examination of older stages probably is to locate the embryo by candling and then to repeatedly tap the egg in the area over the embryo until the shell is extensively cracked, but not broken through. Carefully remove the shell piece by piece to expose the membranes and the embryo.

Refer to Figure 6-17 for a general impression of the relationships of the embryo and extra-embryonic membranes. As you examine the various stages, attempt to sort out the relationships of the membranes in each case. For instance the spreading of the highly vascular allantois and its fusion with the chorion to produce the complex chorio-allantoic membrane can be followed by examining embryos between 5 and 10 days of incubation. Note also the extent to which the yolk sac has enveloped the yolk by later stages. A relative scarcity of vascularization is a very obvious characteristic of the amnion.

2. Following your examination of membrane relationships in each case, dissect the embryo free from the membranes and study external characteristics such as the development of limbs, feather formation, and changing proportional relationships of the parts of the body to one another (Fig. 6-18). Dissection of the embryos will be informative also if time permits. If you decide to dissect an embryo which has been incubated for more than 10 or 12 days, the embryo should be decapitated before dissection is begun. Record notes and sketches of these older embryos for later reference in experimental work. A complete set of photographs of the Hamburger-Hamilton stages of chick development is reproduced in Hamilton (1952).

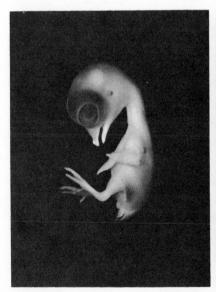

Figure 6-18. Later stages of development of the chick embryo. A. Stage 36 (10 days). B. Stage 38 (12 days). C. Stage 43 (17 days). (The stages are defined by V. Hamburger and H. L. Hamilton, 1951, *J. Morphol.* 88:49-92. Photographs provided by Dr. H. L. Hamilton with the permission of the Wistar Press.)

SUGGESTIONS FOR FURTHER INVESTIGATION

There are many sources from which one can obtain additional basic information on chick development and a number of them are listed in the general references at the end of this chapter. You certainly will want to pursue aspects of induction, morphogenesis, and differentiation in chick development in more detail. Most of these books are written in textbook style, but one of them is a different sort of book and deserves special mention. Romanoff's *The Avian Embryo* is a very detailed source of information on many aspects of chick development. Even if you never use this book for reference purposes, it is well worth the effort to glance through it and to try to imagine the amount of work which went into its preparation.

In the introduction, the long history of studies on the chick embryo was mentioned. If you wish to pursue this history further, consult the historical treatments provided by Needham (1959, 1963), Oppenheimer (1967), and Meyer (1939).

Hopefully, you did not get the impression that our understanding of early chick development is static and that there is universal agreement concerning descriptions of the processes involved because this simply is not the case. For example, Spratt and Haas (1965) have challenged several widely held views of early chick development. They recognize several layers in the pre-primitive streak blastoderm rather than accepting the view that there are two layers, the epiblast and hypoblast. Probably more important, however, is their challenge to traditional views that the primitive streak is a site of cell migration which plays a role comparable to that of the amphibian blastopore. Spratt and Haas contend that the primitive streak is a bud-like proliferation center, or *blastema*. Thus, they argue that the streak is a mitotically active growth center and that cells produced by this proliferative activity migrate away from the streak to take their proper places. They report evidence from cell marking experiments against the notion that cells of the epiblast migrate toward, into, and away from the primitive streak in large numbers. In very extensive studies using tritiated thymidine, however, Rosenquist (1966) obtained results which strongly support the view that the primitive streak is indeed an active migration center. You might find it interesting to read these papers as examples of the problem of interpretation which is inherent in experimental analysis of a relatively familiar and frequently observed developmental process (see also Nicolet, 1971).

There are numerous other areas of disagreement in the literature concerning explanations of various aspects of chick development which might be cited, but we will mention only one additional example. This one was chosen because it relates to a totally different phase of chick development from that considered above. There is a good deal of controversy concerning the method which the chick embryo uses to hatch out of the shell. These arguments involve questions concerning the behavior and physiology of the embryo before and during hatching. There is also disagreement about the role of the "hatching muscle" which is located at the back of the head and neck. This muscle enlarges before the time of hatching and regresses following hatching. Finally, the actual use of the "egg tooth" on the upper beak during the hatching process is still a point of some contention. Access to this interesting literature can be gained through the papers of Smail (1964), Hamburger and Oppenheim (1967), Bock and Hikada (1969), and Brooks and Garrett (1970).

You will find other examples of areas of vigorous research activity concerned with almost every phase of chick development in texts such as Balinsky. In addition to texts, other convenient access routes to research literature on the chick embryo are available. Several chapters in DeHaan and Ursprung (1965) are devoted in part or entirely to chick development at the tissue and organ level of study. Several sections in Bell (1967) contain studies on chick development conducted at the cellular, subcellular and molecular levels. Finally, a number of the reviews in the "Advance in Morphogenesis" series also concern aspects of chick development.

REFERENCES

GENERAL

ABERCROMBIE, M.; BRACHET, J.; and KING, T. J. eds. 1961-1971 (Vols. 1-9). *Advances in morphogenesis.* New York: Academic Press.

AREY, L. B. 1965. *Developmental anatomy.* 7th ed. Philadelphia: Saunders.

BALINSKY, B. I. 1970. *An introduction to embryology.* 3rd ed. Philadelphia: Saunders.

BARTH, L. G. 1953. *Embryology.* New York: Dryden.

BELL, E. ed. 1967. *Molecular and cellular aspects of development.* rev. ed. New York: Harper and Row.

BODEMER, C. W. 1968. *Modern embryology.* New York: Holt, Rinehart and Winston.

DE HAAN, R. L., and URSPRUNG, H. eds. 1965. *Organogenesis.* New York: Holt, Rinehart and Winston.

EBERT, J. D., and SUSSEX, I. M. 1970. *Interacting systems in development.* 2d ed. New York: Holt, Rinehart and Winston.

GILCHRIST, F. G. 1968. *A survey of embryology.* New York: McGraw-Hill.

HAMILTON, H. L. 1952. *Lillie's development of the chick.* 3rd ed. New York: Holt, Rinehart and Winston.

HUETTNER, A. F. 1949. *Fundamentals of comparative embryology of the vertebrates.* rev. ed. New York: Macmillan.

MEYER, A. W. 1939. *The rise of embryology.* Stanford, California: Stanford University Press.

NEEDHAM, J. 1959. *A history of embryology.* 2d ed. New York: Abelard-Schuman.

———. 1963. (Vol. 1). *Chemical embryology.* New York: Hafner. (Reprint of a 1931 publication of Cambridge University Press.)

OPPENHEIMER, J. M. 1967. *Essays in the history of embryology and biology.* Cambridge: M.I.T. Press.

PATTEN, B. M. 1971. *Early embryology of the chick.* 5th ed. New York: McGraw-Hill.

———. 1964. *Foundations of embryology.* New York: McGraw-Hill.

ROMANOFF, A. L. 1960. *The avian embryo.* New York: Macmillan.

RUGH, R. 1964. *Vertebrate embryology.* New York: Harcourt, Brace and World.

SAUNDERS, J. W. JR. 1970. *Patterns and principles of animal development.* New York: Macmillan.

SPECIFIC

BOCK, W. J., and HIKADA, R. S. 1969. Turgidity and function of the hatching muscle. *Amer. Midl. Naturalist* 81:99-106.

BROOKS, W. S., and GARRETT, S. E. 1970. The mechanism of pipping in birds. *The Auk* 87: 458-466.

HAMBURGER, V., and OPPENHEIM, R. 1967. Prehatching motility and hatching behavior in the chick. *Jour. Exp. Zool.* 166:171-204.

NICOLET, G. 1971. Avian gastrulation. *Advances in Morphogenesis* 9:231-262.

ROSENQUIST, G. C. 1966. A radioautographic study of labeled grafts in the chick blastoderm. Development from primitive-streak stages to stage 12. *Carnegie Contribs. Embryol.* 38:71-110.

SMAIL, J. R. 1964. A possible role of the musculus complexus in pipping the chicken egg. *Amer. Midl. Naturalist* 72:499-506.

SPRATT, N. T., JR., and HAAS, H. 1965. Germ layer formation and the role of the primitive streak in the chick. I. Basic architecture and morphogenetic tissue movements. *Jour. Exp. Zool.* 158:9-38.

MATERIALS

EQUIPMENT
Fingerbowls
Syracuse dishes
Watchmaker's forceps
Scissors
"Chick" pipette
Binocular dissecting microscope
Illuminator
Compound microscope
Fine-mouth pipettes (*e.g.*, disposable Pasteur pipettes)
Tungsten microsurgical needle (useful, but not essential)

SOLUTIONS AND CHEMICALS
Howard Ringer (or other chick physiological saline solution)

LIVING MATERIAL
12- to 15-somite embryos (eggs incubated 38-42 hours)
Head-fold embryos (eggs incubated 28-30 hours)
"2-day" embryos (eggs incubated 55-60 hours)
"3-day" embryos (eggs incubated 75-82 hours)
Older embryos—5, 7 or 8, 10, and 17 or 18 days of incubation

COMMERCIALLY PREPARED SLIDES
"33-hour" chick embryo, whole mount
"16-hour" chick embryo, whole mount ("Primitive streak" embryo)
"18-hour" chick embryo, whole mount
"24-hour" chick embryo, whole mount
"33-hour" chick embryo, serial cross sections
"48-hour" chick embryo, whole mount
"72-hour" chick embryo, whole mount

Surgery on the Chick Embryo

Surgical techniques have been used to examine many different developmental interactions in the chick embryo. Numerous experiments have been done at various stages of development to test the effects of altering normal structural relationships between parts of developing embryos. In other experiments, development in the absence of various structures has been studied following complete surgical removal (extirpation). Surgical procedures used on chick embryos are somewhat difficult initially for inexperienced workers, but most students enjoy attempting chick surgery because of its fundamental importance as an experimental method in Developmental Biology. This exercise will serve as an introduction to chick embryo surgery, and the two surgical manipulations suggested here are ones which can give inexperienced workers a modest return in positive results.

The first of these procedures is the removal of part of the developing limb bud of the 3-day embryo. Students generally find it difficult to control precisely the portion of the bud removed, but it is possible to produce a morphologically deficient or abnormal limb by removing a substantial part of the limb bud. Some of the abnormalities produced may mimic certain genetically induced limb abnormalities. It also is possible that some of your results will be similar to those obtained in the classical surgical experiments which have been done on the developing limb (see Suggestions section).

The second of these surgical manipulations is the disruption of the normally closed neural tube of the 3-day chick embryo in the posterior spinal cord region. Because the normal development of the vertebral column is dependent upon the structural integrity of the spinal cord, surgical reopening of the neural tube at this stage of development can lead to production of the condition known as *spina bifida*. This syndrome ranges in severity from minor malformations of the vertebrae to such severe abnormalities as

111

A. CUTTING WINDOW IN EGG

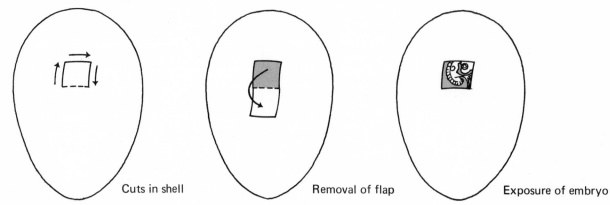

Cuts in shell   Removal of flap   Exposure of embryo

B. REMOVAL OF LIMB BUD   C. SPINA BIFIDA PRODUCTION

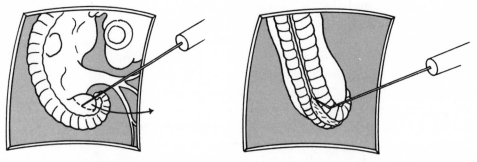

Figure 7-1. A. Steps in the production of a "window" in the egg shell. B. Removal of a portion of the limb bud of a 3-day chick embryo. C. Disruption of a posterior portion of the neural tube of a 3-day chick embryo.

protruberance of the virtually unprotected spinal cord at the surface of the back. *Spina bifida,* by the way, is a relatively common human birth defect.

TECHNIQUES

A. General Surgical Procedures

Directions 1 through 6 below are general ones which apply to either surgical technique. Sections *B* and *C* describe the two surgical procedures. A brief review of the structural relationships of the embryo, the extraembryonic membranes, and the egg would help you in following these directions.

1. Wash the table surface in your work area. Set up your equipment and instruments around your dissecting microscope in what you consider to be a convenient arrangement. Be careful to keep your instrument jar away from your alcohol lamp in order to avoid ignition of the alcohol in the jar. Whenever you remove instruments from the jar, flame off the alcohol by igniting it over the alcohol lamp to complete sterilization. Avoid tipping instruments up in such a way that flaming alcohol runs back onto your fingers. It is difficult to see the clear blue flame of burning alcohol; and, thus, it is relatively easy to receive a painful burn. Avoid accidental transfer of flaming instruments to the instrument jar!

2. You will need to prepare an approximately 1 cm square "window" in the egg to gain access to the embryo. Set the egg in a styrofoam egg nest and work in an area which is slightly nearer the blunt end of the egg than the other end. Swab the area with a piece of cotton dampened (not soaked!) with alcohol from your instrument jar. After the area has dried, begin to cut into the shell with a sharpened hacksaw blade. During this sawing, hold the fingernail of your index finger against the edge of the blade as a guide to keep the cutting edge from sliding around on the surface of the shell. The cut is deep enough when the blade feels as if it is "catching" rather than sawing smoothly. This process should be repeated twice more in order to leave cuts on three sides of a square "window" (Fig. 7-1A).

3. Flame a single-edge razor blade and slip it under the cut opposite the uncut side of the square. A gentle lifting motion should flip back a small piece of shell which can be discarded. If you experience difficulty in lifting the shell, your hacksaw cuts may have to be deepened.

4. Removal of this piece of shell will reveal the shell membranes. Do not be misled by the use of the plural, "membranes," as the shell membranes are closely applied to one another and can be removed together in a single step. Squirt a small volume of sterile saline solution on the membanes to wash away small shell remnants which may be left on their surface. It is also helpful to rock the egg back and forth to free any minor adhesions of embryonic membranes to shell membranes. Peel the shell membranes off with your watchmaker's forceps. In order to prevent damage to underlying structures, puncture the shell membranes with forceps held at a very oblique angle and make certain that penetration is only to the minimal depth necessary to grasp the membranes. The membranes usually can be removed in a series of small strips. If you lose hold of a strip and drop it on the underlying embryo or membranes, retrieve it carefully to avoid injury to delicate structures. You may need to add a drop of saline if this happens because strips of shell membranes tend to stick to embryonic membranes and sometimes must be floated free.

5. Adjust your light source to give the best possible illumination of the embryo. You may detect a reflection of light off the vitelline membrane over the body of the embryo. This membrane is easily punctured with a microsurgical needle and you needn't worry if you are not certain that you really see it. The surgical procedures which are described separately below require the use of

113

your tungsten needle. Do not risk the point of the needle by dipping it in the instrument jar as a brief excursion through the alcohol flame is adequate to sterilize it. Contact with the shell edges around your "window" will also break off the tip of your needle.

6. When you have completed your surgery, cover the hole with one or two strips of cellophane tape and return the egg in its nest to the incubator. Make certain that the egg is firmly closed with tape because drying can be a problem. It sometimes takes several pieces of tape to seal the opening.

B. Extirpation of the Limb Bud

Cut away a portion of the right leg bud with either your tungsten needle or your watch-maker's forceps (Fig. 7-1B). You may find it necessary to use both instruments to hold the bud steady and cut it. There is a tendency to be too conservative in an operation such as this. Try to take out a substantial chunk of the bud. The piece must be cut away cleanly because if it is left partially attached, the great healing powers of the embryo can come into play and produce an essentially normal limb. Close the egg as quickly as you can after you finish your work.

Record the results of the operation in a simple sketch of the limb bud made after surgery. You should make notes on the operation so that you have a reference later when you examine the results or in the case of death of the embryo. Each egg should be marked or numbered so that you can identify it specifically. Carefully avoid puncturing the yolk sac during the limb-bud operation because of yolk-sac puncture usually results in the death of the embryo. You may wish to use some of your embryos for wing-bud rather than the leg-bud operations. You might also wish to repeat some of the classical experiments on apical ectoderm removal (see especially Zwilling, 1961), but such operations require much more skill than the simple removal of a roughly defined portion of the bud.

C. Disruption of the Neural Tube

Spina bifida can be induced experimentally by cutting open a posterior section of the neural tube of the 3-day chick embryo. When the tube is cut open at this stage, reclosure does not occur and there is a permanent disruption of normal structural relationships. You must use great care in this operation because the dorsal aorta lies only a short distance below the neural tube and puncture of the aorta kills the embryo. You may expect some bleeding from smaller vessels, but if you see large spurts of blood in the area of the needle, you should discard the egg and begin again with another one.

Use a very fine tungsten needle which has its tip bent at an angle to cut open a small section of the neural tube at about the level of the leg buds Fig. (7-1C). Attempt to enter the tube from a posterior direction. If your needle tip actually enters the neural canal, it is easy to open the tube with a lifting movement. At first, however, you may have to do some rather extensive probing of the neural tube in this area, and you may cut the tube open largely by chance. If the tube has been cut successfully, the lateral walls of the tube flatten and the outlines of the tube in that area become indistinct. You may see only the apparent disappearance of the lateral walls of the tube. Continue work on the tube until you think that you have seen some change. Random probing about usually has no effect on neural tube development.

Make notes on each operation so that they can be compared with the results observed when the egg is opened. Include observations on bleeding and other problems which you encounter. Carefully mark eggs so that you will be able to relate survival and results with observations made at the time of the operation.

D. Analysis of Results

1. During the period of further incubation, your instructor may ask you to candle your own eggs and make decisions concerning eggs to be removed from the incubator and discarded. You may expect quite a number of embryos to die following operation, but be conservative in discarding eggs in order to avoid throwing away a good specimen. Open the eggs which you discard and, if possible, determine and record the approximate stage of development at which they died. Your instructor may elect to candle eggs for you.

2. Results of limb bud operations should be taken after about two weeks of further incubation. Check the operated limbs for any growth deficiencies, structural anomalies, or other evidence of abnormal development. Record your observations and, in your notes or discussion, attempt to correlate your results with the types of operations that you did. It is often possible to relate a specific deficiency in the limb to removal of a specific part of the bud. Compare results with those obtained by your classmates. Your instructor may direct you to preserve the embryos and make dissections or other type of observations on the operated limbs.

3. The *spina bifida* embryos should also be opened after two weeks further incubation. It usually is necessary to pluck some feathers from the back to expose a *spina bifida*. You may wish to preserve your specimens in formalin for later observation. If time permits, a dissection of preserved specimens may help to clarify the full extent of any deformity of the spinal cord and surrounding tissues. In your notes or discussion, relate results obtained to observations made during the operations.

SUGGESTIONS FOR FURTHER INVESTIGATION

A number of experimental manipulations of chick embryos are described in Hamburger (1960) and in Rugh (1962). You probably will be impressed by the variety of surgical interventions which embryos will tolerate, and you might wish to attempt some of these other operations.

There is a good deal of controversy concerning interpretation of results of surgical experiments on the roles of the ectodermal and mesodermal components of the limb bud and their interaction in limb development. You can learn more about this problem by consulting the reviews of Zwilling (1961), Amprino (1965), and Milaire (1962). A very interesting aspect of limb morphogenesis is the role of cell death in shaping the definitive limb. Clever surgical manipulations have contributed to understanding of this phenomenon also. Reviews by Saunders (1966) and Saunders and Fallon (1967) deal with this interesting work on populations of cells whose normal developmental fate is death.

It is possible to make preparations of embryos whose skeletal systems have been selectively stained to contrast with the rest of their bodies which have been cleared. Such preparations allow direct observation of the effects of experimental procedures on skeletal system development, and you might wish to use them to study the results of your limb bud surgery. Consult Hamburger (1960), Guyer (1953), or Jensh and Brent (1966) for the selective skeletal staining technique.

There is a method for dissection of embryos following pretreatment in nitric acid which makes possible isolation of a nearly intact central nervous system. These dissections add a great deal to the study of results of operations on the developing nervous system such as your *spina bifida* operation. For description and application of the technique, consult Huber (1936) and Watterson (1949).

Another kind of example of the experimental use of surgery on chick embryos has been in the investigation of endocrine relationships during chick development. It is possible to remove the rudiments of the developing pituitary gland by cutting off the forepart of the head after about 1 1/2 days of incubation. This pituitary removal (or hypophysectomy) by partial decapitation has drastic effects on a variety of structural and physiological aspects of development. Hinni and Watterson

(1963) provide a brief review of a number of these studies on endocrine regulation of developmental processes. You may wish to attempt this surgical procedure. It is not as difficult as you might think, and you may be able to do the operation if you have had some success with other types of surgery. The rather spectacular results of successful operations (stunted embryos lacking eyes and upper beaks) provide a fine reward for the effort.

An interesting example of the use of classical surgical methods in conjunction with the more recently developed technique of autoradiography is the work of Weston (1963, 1970) on behavior of neural crest cells. Neural crest cells are migratory cells which leave the neural tube during early development and move to a variety of sites throughout the embryo where they settle and proliferate to play numerous roles in development. Cells of neural crest origin produce the pigment cells of the body, the cells of the nervous system ganglia, the sheath cells which enclose individual nerve fibers, and a variety of other important cell types. Weston substituted radioactively-labeled sections of neural tube for pieces of neural tube which he removed from embryos at early stages of development. He then sacrificed these host embryos at intervals after the operation and used autoradiographic analysis to trace the migration of labeled neural crest cells away from the grafted section of the neural tube. You can obtain further details of these cleverly executed experiments in his papers.

REFERENCES

GENERAL

HAMBURGER, V. 1960. *A manual of experimental embryology.* Chicago: University of Chicago Press.

RUGH, R. 1962. *Experimental embryology.* 3rd ed. Minneapolis: Burgess.

SPECIFIC

AMPRINO, R. 1965. Aspects of limb morphogenesis in the chicken. In *Organogenesis*, R. L. DeHaan and H. Ursprung eds. New York: Holt, Rinehart and Winston.

GUYER, M. F. 1953. Staining the skeletons of cleared embryos. In *Animal Micrology*. 5th ed. Chicago: University of Chicago Press, pp. 148-149.

HINNI, J. B., and WATTERSON, R. L. 1963. Modified development of the duodenum of chick embryos hypophysectomized by partial decapitation. *Jour. Morph.* 113:381-426.

HUBER, J. F. 1936. Nerve roots and nuclear groups in the spinal cord of the pigeon. *Jour. Comp. Neurology* 65:43-91.

JENSH, R. P., and BRENT, R. L. 1966. Rapid schedules for KOH clearing and Alizarin Red S staining of fetal rat bone. *Stain Technology* 41:179-183.

MILAIRE, J. 1962. Histochemical aspects of limb morphogenesis in vertebrates. *Advances in Morphogenesis* 2:183-209.

SAUNDERS, J. W. JR. 1966. Cell death in embryonic systems. *Science* 154:604-612.

SAUNDERS, J. W. JR., and FALLON, J. F. 1967. Cell death in morphogenesis. In *Major Problems in Developmental Biology*, M. Locke ed. New York: Academic Press.

WATTERSON, R. L. 1949. Development of the glycogen body of the chick spinal cord. I. Normal morphogenesis, vasculogenesis and anatomical relationships. *Jour. Morph.*, 85:337-390.

WESTON, J. A. 1963. A radioautographic analysis of the migration and localization of trunk neural crest cells in the chick. *Develop. Biol.* 6:279-310.

———. 1970. The migration and differentiation of neural crest cells. *Advances in Morphogenesis* 8:41-114.

ZWILLING, E. 1961. Limb morphogenesis. *Advances in Morphogenesis* 1:301-330.

119

MATERIALS

EQUIPMENT
"Egg nests"
Illuminator
Binocular dissecting microscope
Sharpened hacksaw blade
Single-edge razor blade
Clean disposable Pasteur pipettes
Instrument jar
Alcohol lamp
Absorbent cotton
Tungsten (or glass) microsurgical needle
Cellophane tape

SOLUTIONS AND CHEMICALS
Howard Ringer (or other chick physiological saline solution)

LIVING MATERIAL
Eggs incubated 72 hours (or slightly longer, See Appendix D)

Chorio-allantoic Membrane Grafting

Transplantation to the chorio-allantoic membrane (CAM) of the developing chick embryo provides a means of isolating embryonic or other tissues from their normal environment while still permitting further growth and differentiation. This technique has somewhat different applications than rigorously controlled *in vitro* culture methods because in CAM grafting the environment provided for the tissue under study cannot be defined precisely. For instance, hormones in the embryonic circulation reach the graft on the CAM. The CAM grafting technique, however, is much easier to use than most *in vitro* tissue culture techniques. The extraembryonic site provides a very favorable environment for maintenance and further development of the tissue under study, and the elaborate preparatory steps of the *in vitro* approach are unnecessary. The extraembryonic fluids make a suitable "medium," and if the graft "takes" effectively, blood vessels of the host's extraembryonic circulation will grow into and vascularize the graft. The embryonic circulation will then transport nutrients and oxygen to the graft and carry metabolic wastes away from it.

This laboratory is an introduction to the techniques of CAM grafting.

TECHNIQUES

A. Preparation of Hosts

1. Eggs which have been incubated for 9 and 10 days will serve as hosts. Candle the eggs to locate and mark an area where you can see a Y-shaped junction of blood vessels in the CAM (see Figure 8-1A and "Candling" in Appendix D). Some workers maintain that such junctions are the best sites for grafts. After marking the eggs, proceed with your preparation by placing a "window" in the shells of several host embryos.

123

A. EXTERNAL VIEW OF EGG
USING CANDLER

air space

"Y" region with rich
blood supply

embryo

B. PLACING OF GRAFT
THROUGH WINDOW

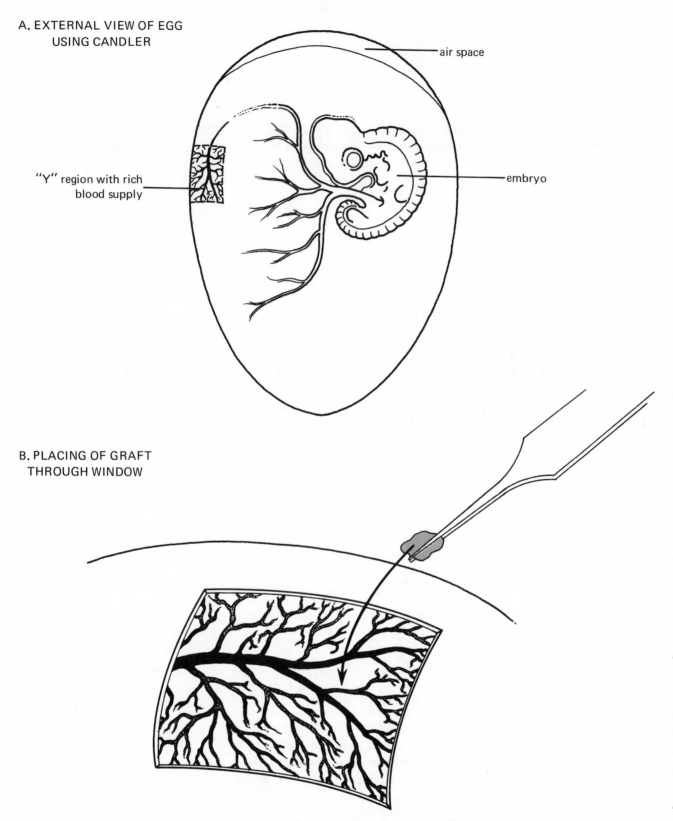

Figure 8-1. A. Marking a Y-shaped junction of CAM blood vessels located by candling. B. Transfer of a graft to the CAM.

2. The technique for opening the shell is basically the same as that described in Exercise 7 ("Surgery on the Chick Embryo"). However, several additional steps are required. Before you begin sawing the shell, you should puncture the air space at the egg's blunt end. Puncture of the air space causes the CAM to drop away ("lower") at the time that the window is cut. This membrane lowering helps to prevent damage during subsequent manipulations. After you have swabbed the blunt end of the egg with alcohol, stick the needle of a wooden-handle probe about 1/2 cm into the egg's blunt end. You must exercise cautious control of the probe during this step because it takes some pressure to puncture the shell, but it is easy to drive the needle right on through the air space into the interior of the egg.

Proceed with "window" cutting after you have punctured the air space. When the window is complete, cover it and the hole in the blunt end with pieces of cellophane tape until the donor material has been prepared. Return the host eggs to the incubator during this time.

B. Preparation of Donor Tissue

1. Donor tissue can be taken from chick embryos of a variety of ages. Parts of early embryos give more spectacular results because of the marked degree of change which occurs during the culture period. On the other hand, tissues from older embryos are easier to dissect and transfer to the CAM. Some tissues which give good results are eyes or posterior portions of 48-hour embryos and limb buds of 72-hour embryos. Back tissue from older embryos (5 or 6 days of incubation) will also develop well and should produce feathers.

2. Donor embryos can be cut up in a Syracuse dish of Howard Ringer. Cross dissecting needles over the body of the donor. Keep the tips against the bottom of the dish and draw the needles across one another scissors fashion. After one or two trials, you should become adept enough at slicing up the body of the donor to prepare the specific pieces which you wish to use. One donor can be used to provide tissue for several grafts.

C. Transplantation

1. Reopen a host egg when you are ready to transfer a piece of tissue. Focus your light source on the window so that you can see the blood vessels of the CAM clearly. Transfer the tissue with a watchmaker's forceps and put it in place over the blood vessel junction which you located previously (Fig. 8-1B). It is also possible to use a fine-mouth pipette to transfer the tissue, but the saline carried along in the pipette tends to float the tissue off the selected position. If the graft slips out of sight to the side of the hole or seems to "disappear," transplant a second piece of tissue to the site. Such lost pieces of tissue rarely "show up" and should be replaced. Retape the shell as quickly as possible to avoid further desiccation and return it to the incubator.

2. Number your host eggs and record the size and type of graft transplanted to each one. Make note of any unusual observations or any problems such as bleeding which you encounter during the procedure. Record also the position of the graft relative to blood vessels.

D. Analysis of Results

1. After 7 days of further incubation, open each egg to "harvest" the graft. It is best to remove the cellophane tape and enlarge the window by picking away the shell piece by piece. As you remove small pieces of shell, watch carefully for evidence of the growing graft on the CAM. Successful grafts usually will be easy to detect as rather large masses of tissue on the membrane. If the graft has not "taken" and has degenerated, you usually will see a small reddish-brown or black spot. A few grafts simply will be lost and you will find no trace of them, but you should not discard the host until you have examined all parts of the CAM carefully. Remove each successful graft by cutting it out of the CAM. Include a large enough circle of CAM tissue to permit handling without touching the graft itself. Preserve each graft in formalin and label the jar with the number of the host egg and information about the graft. Decapitate host embryos before discarding them.

2. Carefully examine the grafts under the binocular microscope. Sketch each graft, measure its size, and identify as many structures as possible. In your notes or discussion, compare the extent and "normality" of the graft with development of the comparable part of an intact embryo over the same period of time. Possibly, some extra donor embryos will have been left in the incubator for purposes of comparison.

SUGGESTIONS FOR FURTHER INVESTIGATION

A number of chick grafting techniques which you might wish to attempt are described in Hamburger (1960) and Rugh (1962).

Although it has been demonstrated that diverse tissues from donors ranging from frog to man can be grown on the chick CAM, the most extensive use of this technique has been in experimental analysis of chick development. The work of Mary Rawles (1936, 1943, 1952) provides an excellent example of the kind of results which can be obtained using this technique. She divided early chick embryos into carefully defined parts and grew these pieces as CAM grafts. She sectioned the grafts and examined them histologically in order to determine what tissue types could be detected in grafts derived from each part of the blastoderm. By careful and repeated replications of these experiments, she was able to catalogue the developmental potentials of various parts of the blastoderm. You may wish to attempt further experimentation on the ability of parts of very young embryos to carry on independent development and differentiation on the CAM.

In experiments on interaction of ectodermal and mesodermal components from various skin areas, Rawles (1963) found that drying caused some abnormal developmental patterns. She modified conventional CAM techniques by adding fluid (albumen and saline in a 15:1 mixture) daily to keep the graft submerged. This treatment caused the membrane to rise and brought the graft nearer the opening in the shell. In order to accommodate this rising membrane, she constructed a "chimney" device over the original shell opening You might find this paper interesting because of the technical modification of CAM grafting reported in it, and also because it is another excellent example of application of CAM grafting to the experimental analysis of development.

Weiss and Taylor (1960) applied CAM grafting to problems of behavior and interaction of individual embryonic cells. They dissociated cells from organs of relatively advanced chick embryos (8 to 14 days of incubation) and centrifuged the cell suspensions into lumps which were transplanted to the CAM. Sectioning of the aggregates after further development on the CAM revealed that there had been reorganization into tissues characteristic of the organs from which the cells had come. For example, mesonephros aggregates developed apparently normal kidney tubules and skin aggregates produced feathers. Thus, CAM grafting was teamed with techniques of cell dissociation to demonstrate that dissociated cells from organs in advanced stages of differentiation still possessed the ability to reaggregate and reorganize into histologically normal tissues. You may wish to compare this work with that of Moscona (see Exercise 4 for references) which concentrated on very

early organ rudiments. The work of Weiss and Taylor is of particular interest because it opened the possibility of using the CAM to replace elaborate and expensive culture arrangements in dissociation experiments. This could make experiments on dissociated cells of embryonic homeotherms possible for interested Developmental Biology students.

Still another application of CAM grafting was reported by Betz (1967, 1970) and Bellware and Betz (1970) in work with embryos which had been decapitated at 1 1/2 days of incubation (see Exercise 7 "Suggestions" section). They transplanted pituitary glands to the CAM of these decapitated (hypophysectomized) embryos and found that the grafted embryonic pituitary glands reversed developmental deficiencies caused by pituitary deprivation in the operated embryos.

Many other studies in Developmental Biology have involved grafting to the CAM (*e.g.*, Bradley, 1970). You will undoubtedly encounter more of these experiments if you do further reading in the experimental analysis of chick development. Possibly, you will want to test various hypotheses of your own using isolation of tissues on the CAM.

REFERENCES

GENERAL

HAMBURGER, V. 1960. *A manual of experimental embryology.* Chicago: University of Chicago Press.
RUGH, R. 1962. *Experimental embryology.* 3rd ed. Minneapolis: Burgess.

SPECIFIC

BELLWARE, F. T., and BETZ, T. W. 1970. The dependence of duodenal differentiation in chick embryos on pars distalis hormones. *Jour. Embryol. Exp. Morph.* 24:335-355.
BETZ, T. W. 1967. The effects of embryonic pars distalis grafts on the development of hypophysectomized chick embryos. *Gen. Comp. Endocrinol.* 9:172-186.
———. 1970. The developmental endocrinology of the spleen in chick embryos. I. The pars distalis. *Jour. Embryol. Exp. Morph.* 24:357-365.
BRADLEY, S. J. 1970. An analysis of self-differentiation of chick limb buds in chorio-allantoic grafts. *Jour. Anat.* 107:479-490.
RAWLES, M. E. 1936. A study of the localization of organ-forming areas in the chick blastoderm. *Jour. Exp. Zool.* 72:271-315.
———. 1943. The heart-forming areas of the early chick blastoderm. *Physiol. Zool.* 16:22-42.
———. 1952. On transplantation of normal embryonic tissues. *Ann. N.Y. Acad. Sci.* 55:302-312.
———. 1963. Tissue interactions in scale and feather development as studied in dermal-epidermal recombinations. *Jour. Embryol. Exp. Morph.* 11:765-789.
WEISS, P., and TAYLOR, A. C. 1960. Reconstitution of complete organs from single-cell suspensions of chick embryos in advanced stages of differentiation. *Proc. Nat. Acad. Sci.* 46:1177-1185.

MATERIALS

EQUIPMENT

Candler
"Egg nests"
Wooden-handle probes (dissecting needles)
Sharpened hacksaw blade
Single-edge razor blade
Watchmaker's forceps
Scissors
Instrument jar
Alcohol lamp
Absorbent cotton
Cellophane tape
Fingerbowls
Syracuse dishes
Binocular dissecting microscope
Illuminator

SOLUTIONS AND CHEMICALS

Howard Ringer (or other chick physiological saline solution)

LIVING MATERIAL

Eggs incubated 9 or 10 days (hosts)
Donor embryos (see section *B* for suggested incubation stages)

In <u>vitro</u> Culture of Chick Embryos

There are many questions in Developmental Biology which can be answered only when cells, tissues, or organs can be removed from their normal environment within the developing organism. These questions may concern the ability of the particular part to carry on independent development or the effects of a particular experimental treatment on the part being studied. Attacks on such problems have been made using a number of kinds of culture techniques. Isolated parts, or *explants,* are maintained in various precisely defined media in culture vessels made of glass (literally *in vitro*) or plastic. The important common factor in these techniques is that responses are tested in the absence of complicated interactions with other parts of the developing system.

Unfortunately, culture media usually provide a very favorable environment for the growth of a variety of bacteria and molds. Thus, most culture work requires considerable technical skill applied under rigorously controlled environmental conditions which are hard to provide in a teaching laboratory. This persistent threat of infection and overgrowth by microorganisms is a discouraging factor in culture studies, but the embryo culture techniques devised by Spratt (1947) circumvent many of the difficulties met in other types of culture work because the medium contains egg white which has antibacterial properties. Of course, culture of whole blastoderms or large parts of blastoderms by the Spratt technique as described here is fundamentally different from those types of culture work in which only small parts of embryos are transferred. Furthermore, it is not possible to define the contents of the Spratt culture medium in precise chemical terms. However, "Spratt culturing" is a useful general introduction to *in vitro* culture technique.

133

TECHNIQUES

A. Preparation of Culture Medium

Prepare your work area as you did for Exercise 7 ("Surgery on the Chick Embryo").

Because preparation of materials is such a critically important part of any culture study, your instructor may wish to have you prepare your own culture medium and culture chambers. Preparative techniques are described in Directions 1 through 3 below. If your instructor provides culture vessels made up in advance, skip to Section *B*.

1. Prepare culture vessels with a watch glass mounted on a ring of damp cotton inside a petri dish (see Figure 9-1). The cotton should be soaked and then gently rung out before it is formed into a ring. This damp cotton helps to keep the humidity high in the culture "chamber." If you are using semi-sterile techniques, these vessels and the saline solution to be used in medium preparation should be sterilized in an autoclave, but sterilization of the vessels is not absolutely essential as reasonably good results can be obtained without sterilization.

2. The two major components of the medium (Solution *A* and Solution *B*) are prepared in separate steps and mixed just before it is poured into the watch glasses in the culture chambers.

    a. *Preparation of Solution A.* Combine 50 ml of Howard Ringer (see Appendix D), or other appropriate chick embryo saline solution, with the white of one egg in a capped container. Shake the mixture vigorously and set it aside in a cool place until the saline-agar-glucose component has been prepared.

    b. *Preparation of Solution B.* Place 0.4 gm of plain agar (*not* "nutrient agar") and 70 cc of Howard Ringer in a flask and heat the mixture to boiling with continuous stirring. Cool this mixture after it has come to a boil and as it cools add and stir in 1 gm of glucose. When this mixture has cooled to about 45°C, you are ready to combine the two components and pour the medium into the culture vessels.

3. Add 30 ml of Solution *A* (saline-albumin component) to Solution *B* (saline-agar-glucose mixture). Pour Solution *A* carefully so that the frothy material on the surface is excluded from the final mixture. Swirl the medium to mix the components thoroughly.

Proceed with pouring the medium at once because the agar may begin to solidify rather quickly with further cooling. Pour enough medium into each watch glass to provide a surface area which is at least 2.5 cm in diameter. If you are using semi-sterile techniques throughout and do not know proper petri dish pouring technique, check with your instructor for guidance. The culture vessels may be stored in the refrigerator if necessary. If culture vessels have been refrigerated, however, they should be allowed to warm to room temperature before use. One final note of caution is that vessels should be handled carefully after they have been poured because the medium tends to "slip around" in the watch glasses and may even slide over the edges if the dishes are tilted too much.

CROSS SECTION OF CULTURE VESSEL

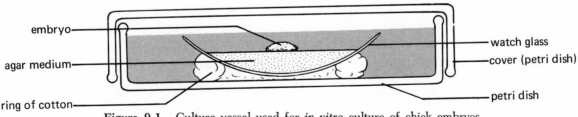

Figure 9-1. Culture vessel used for *in vitro* culture of chick embryos.

B. Explantation of Embryos

1. After preparing or receiving culture vessels, proceed with explantation of the embryos. For each culture, remove the blastoderm from a fertile egg incubated for about 24 hours using the same technique which you used earlier in the examination of living embryos (See Exercise 6: "Patterns of Chick Development"). Use warm Howard Ringer solution for all steps requiring "saline" in the procedure described in Exercise 6. To reduce the risk of bacterial and fungal infections further, 100 mg each of sulfadiazine (USP Powder, Lederle) and Mycostatin (100,000 units/g, Squibb) may be added to a liter of the Howard Ringer solution.

When the blastoderm has been transferred to the Syracuse dish, you may have to spend some time carefully removing yolk granules and freeing the blastoderm from the vitelline membrane. Try to work efficiently, however, because it is best to avoid unnecessarily extensive or prolonged handling of the blastoderm.

Some workers claim to obtain better results if they transect the blastoderm and discard the portion anterior to the head. This trimming can be accomplished with a pair of steel needles (clean, flamed dissecting needles are adequate for this). If two needles are crossed over the blastoderm with the tips kept on the bottom of the Syracuse dish, drawing the needles across one another will produce a scissors action which should cut the blastoderm cleanly. Don't trim other sides of the blastoderm too closely, however, because you will obtain poor results if you fail to include a substantial part of the area opaca in each explant.

2. Make certain that you keep the petri dishes open no longer than is absolutely essential for transfer and positioning of the blastoderm.

Re-wet your "chick" pipette and transfer the blastoderm to the culture chamber. Gently spread the blastoderm with your forceps. It is desirable to leave some saline around the blastoderm, but you may need to remove excess saline in order to flatten the blastoderm. Excess saline should be drawn off very carefully with a Pasteur pipette to avoid damage to the blastoderm.

3. Mark the culture vessels so that you can identify each of your cultures. Make a rough sketch of the embryo in each case as you observe it against a dark background. Note such features as somite number, head folding, neural development, and any other characteristics which you observe. Make certain that you record whether the dorsal or ventral surface of the blastoderm is in contact with the surface of the medium in each case.

If you have several culture dishes to use and find that you are becoming adept at transferring blastoderms, you may wish to cut up a blastoderm and attempt culture of the fragments.

4. Place the culture vessels in the incubator.

C. Analysis of Results

1. Observe your cultures after 24 hours in the incubator. Make rough sketches of the embryos and determine their developmental stages as accurately as you can. Stage them using the Hamburger-Hamilton stages or a morphological criterion such as somite number rather than making arbitrary statements about ages in terms of hours or days of incubation. Compare the rate of development *in vitro* with the rate in the egg (*in ovo*). Possibly your instructor will be able to provide some eggs which were not used for cultures. You might find it helpful in considering developmental rates to open some of these eggs and stage the embryos.

Return the embryos to the incubator as quickly as possible for further incubation. Discard cultures in which the embryos clearly have failed to develop or which show signs of gross contamination (milky, white bacterial colonies are obvious signs of contamination). Be cautious about discarding any uncontaminated cultures, however, because grossly abnormal development can be very interesting. Look carefully for any sign of development such as a misshapen, but nevertheless pulsating heart tube.

2. Observe your cultures at the end of a second day of incubation and record observations in the same way that you did at the end of the first day. By this time you may expect contamination of a fairly large percentage of the cultures, particularly if only minimal precautions were taken to preserve sterility.

SUGGESTIONS FOR FURTHER INVESTIGATION

Further information on embryo culturing by the "Spratt technique" can be obtained in Rugh (1962). DeHaan (1967) describes avian embryo culture techniques and provides references to some studies which have used culture techniques to attack various developmental problems. New (1966) has compiled a broader treatment of the culture of various vertebrate embryos.

Culture techniques have been used by Spratt and others to study metabolic characteristics of the chick embryo. Some examples of these studies are Spratt's experiments on the embryo's ability to metabolize various substrates (Spratt, 1949, 1950a, 1950b) and on the effects of metabolic inhibitors on various aspects of development (Spratt, 1950b). Several workers (Rothfels, 1954; Klein et al., 1962; Von Hahn and Herrmann, 1962) have studied amino acid metabolism in chick development using culture techniques. Ebert (1952) examined the appearance of organ-specific antigens at various developmental stages in cultured embryos. You may think of possibilities for further investigation as you read some of these papers.

Another interesting and highly useful technique for embryo culture was developed by New (New, 1955, 1966; DeHaan, 1967). This technique involves transfer of the vitelline membrane along with the blastoderm to a liquid culture. With the "New technique," it is possible to avoid some of the distortion of embryos which frequently is caused by semi-solid culture media. You may be interested in comparing results obtained using the "Spratt" and "New" techniques. Gallera (1971) has included a comparison of various culture methods as part of a review of the results of experiments on primary induction which were done with cultured embryos.

You may recall from Exercise 6 ("Patterns of Chick Development") that culture techniques were used in studying cell migrations in early development. More recently, Rosenquist has used autoradiographic labeling of embryos cultured by the "New technique" to determine origins of cells which ultimately produce various organs in the embryo (e.g., Rosenquist, 1971).

Long-distance individual cell migrations such as those of the primordial germ cells have been studied in cultured embryos. These cells migrate through the embryo, lodge in the developing gonads, and give rise to the gametes which ultimately develop in the gonads (see Exercise 5 for discussion of the primordial germ cells in amphibian embryos). This fascinating research has been summarized by Barth (1964), but some of the original sources make very interesting reading if they are available. Simon (1960) used culture of whole and part embryos to do beautiful, detailed studies on the migration of the chick embryo germ cells. Should you become interested in pursuing chick germ cell migration further, several additional references are available. DuBois (see DuBois, 1969, for access to literature) has examined mechanisms involved in the migration process. The behavior and properties of germ cells in later stages of chick development have been studied by Hughes (see Hughes 1963, 1964). Further experiments on this system, particularly those involving embryo culture, may suggest themselves as you read these references. According to Singh and Meyer (1967), it is possible to identify germ cells in smears and squashes of cells from the avian embryo. Thus, it may not always be necessary to make histological preparations in order to assess results of experimental studies on chick primordial germ cells.

139

REFERENCES

GENERAL

DeHaan, R. L. 1967. Avian embryo culture. In *Methods in developmental biology*, F. H. Wilt and N. K. Wessells eds. New York: Thomas Y. Crowell, pp. 401-412.

New, D. A. T. 1966. *The culture of vertebrate embryos.* London: Logos Press.

Paul, J. 1965. *Cell and tissue culture.* Baltimore: Williams and Wilkins.

Rugh, R. 1962. *Experimental embryology.* Minneapolis: Burgess.

White, P. R. 1963. *The culture of animal and plant cells.* 2d ed. New York: Ronald Press.

Willmer, E. N. 1965. *Cells and tissues in culture.* New York: Academic Press.

SPECIFIC

Barth, L. J. 1964. *Development: selected topics.* Reading, Mass.: Addison-Wesley.

DuBois, R. 1969. Le mécanisme d'entrée des cellules germinales primordiales dans le réseau vasculaire, chez l'embryon de Poulet. *Jour. Embryol. Exp. Morph.* 21:255-270.

Ebert, J. D. 1952. Appearance of tissue-specific proteins during development. *Ann. N.Y. Acad. Sci.* 55: 67-84.

Gallera, J. 1971. Primary induction in birds. *Advances in Morphogenesis* 9:149-180.

Hughes, G. C. 1963. The population of germ cells in the developing female chick. *Jour. Embryol. Exp. Morph.* 11:513-536.

————. 1964. The radiosensitivity of oögonia and oöcytes in the chick embryo. *Jour. Embryol. Exp. Morph.* 12:273-287.

Klein, N. W.; McConnell, E.; Buckingham, B. J. 1962. Growth of explanted chick embryos on a chemically defined medium and effects of specific amino acid deficiencies. *Develop. Biol.* 5:296-308.

New, D. A. T. 1955. A new technique for the cultivation of the chick embryo *in vitro. Jour. Embryol. Exp. Morph.* 3:326-331.

Rosenquist, G. C. 1971. The location of the pregut endoderm in the chick embryo at the primitive streak stage as determined by radioautographic mapping. *Develop. Biol.* 26:323-335.

Rothfels, U. 1954. The effects of some amino acid analogues on the development of the chick embryo *in vitro. Jour. Exp. Zool.* 125:17-37.

Simon, D. 1970. Contribution a l'etude de la circulation et du transport des gonocytes primaires dans les blastodermes d'oiseau cultivés *in vitro Arch. Anat. Microscop. Morphol. Exp.* 49:93-176.

Singh, R. P., and Meyer, D. B. 1967. Primordial germ cells in blood smears from chick embryos. *Science* 156:1503-1504.

Spratt, N. T., Jr. 1947. Development *in vitro* of the early chick blastoderm explanted on yolk and albumen extract saline-agar medium. *Jour. Exp. Zool.* 106:345-366.

————. 1949. Nutritional requirements of the early chick embryo. I. The utilization of carbohydrate substrates. *Jour. Exp. Zool.* 110:273-298.

————. 1950a. Nutritional requirements of the early chick embryo. II. Differential nutrient requirements for morphogenesis and differentiation of the heart and brain. *Jour. Exp. Zool.* 114:375-402.

————. 1950b. Nutritional requirements of the early chick embryo. III. The metabolic basis of morphogenesis and differentiation as revealed by the use of inhibitors. *Biol. Bull.* 99:120-135.

Von Hahn, H. P., and Herrmann, H. 1962. Effects of amino acid analogs on growth and catheptic activity of chick embryo explants. *Develop. Biol.* 5:309-327.

MATERIALS

EQUIPMENT
Erlenmeyer flasks (for medium preparation)
Culture dishes (see Section A)
Fingerbowls
Syracuse dishes
Scissors
Watchmaker's forceps
"Chick" pipette
Disposable Pasteur pipettes
Wooden-handle probes (dissecting needles)
Instrument jar
Alcohol lamp
Binocular dissecting microscope
Illuminator

SOLUTIONS AND CHEMICALS
Howard Ringer
Unincubated eggs
Agar (plain agar, not "nutrient agar")
Glucose

LIVING MATERIAL
Eggs incubated for 24 hours

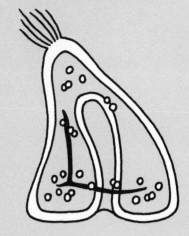

Fertilization and Early Development of the Sea Urchin

Two distinct functions are served by the act of fertilization. The first is concerned with the initiation of a complicated series of morphological and physiological changes in the egg itself. These changes in the properties of the egg lead to cleavage and the further development of the embryo. This aspect of fertilization is often termed *activation*. The second function is concerned with the hereditary mechanism: the union of male and female pronuclei that restores the diploid number of chromosomes upon which biparental inheritance is based.

A considerable amount of research in Developmental Biology has dealt with the physico-chemical aspects of the activation of the egg, and much of the experimental work has been done on the eggs of sea urchins and starfish. These echinoderms are abundantly available; their gametes can be obtained readily in great quantities, and developing eggs can be cultured in simple media.

Among the changes that accompany the union of sperm and egg may be included (a) the formation and regression of the *fertilization cone* which is concerned with sperm penetration, (b) the rearrangement (disappearance of some) of *cortical granules* which is related to the formation of the *fertilization membrane*, (c) the elevation of the vitelline membrane, beginning at the point of sperm contact, to form the fertilization membrane, (d) the appearance of the *perivitelline space* between the egg and the fertilization membrane, and (e) the formation of the viscous *hyaline layer* which adheres closely to the surface of the egg.

This exercise concentrates on the visibly observable events of fertilization and succeeding stages of early development in the sea urchin.

145

TECHNIQUES

A. Procurement of Gametes

As in other echinoderms, the sexes are separate in sea urchins. In nature, gametes are discharged into the water, and the sperm swim freely before they reach the egg. One of the more widely studied species is the west coast purple urchin, *Strongylocentrotus purpuratus*. Its gametes can be obtained in great abundance from December through March.

Unfortunately, the sexes of the sea urchin cannot be distinguished by any external feature. However, injection of a small amount of potassium chloride into the coelom will induce the urchin to shed its gametes. The sex of the animal can then be determined by observing the color of gametes extruded from pores of the aboral (dorsal) surface of the animal within a few minutes after injection. The eggs of *Strongylocentrotus purpuratus* are translucent yellow to pale orange while the sperm in mass appear white or light gray.

You should be cautioned that the gametes and embryos are extremely sensitive to temperatures above 15°C. The culture medium (seawater) should not be allowed to warm above 15°C.

1. Place adult urchins in individual Syracuse dishes with the aboral ("opposite to, or away from, the mouth") surface down. Induce shedding of gametes by injecting 1 or 2 ml of 0.5 M KCl through the membrane surrounding the oral opening (perioral, or peristomial, membrane). To insure entrance of KCl into the perivisceral coelom, it may be advisable to inject through several points in the perioral membrane. Avoid possible contamination of eggs with sperm by using a separate syringe and needle for each animal, or rinsing the same syringe and needle with boiling water before each injection.

2. The yellow-orange eggs may be collected by inverting the female over a finger bowl or a beaker of cold (10°C-12°C) seawater. The water level in the beaker should be such that the genital pores ("gonadopores") of the female are covered with water. The eggs will flow out of the gonadopores and settle to the bottom of the beaker. The eggs should be "washed" by decanting the supernatant water and replacing it with a fresh supply of cold seawater. This procedure is intended to remove coelomic fluid, broken spines, and body surface debris from the water. Because coelomic fluid hinders the fertilization process, the eggs should be washed at least twice. Some workers collect gametes from the aboral surface with a pipette to avoid such contamination.

These washed eggs are ready for fertilization. The eggs can be stored at 5°C for 12 hours without loss in fertilizability. A thin layer of scattered eggs in the bottom of the finger bowl is an appropriate egg density. In order to achieve a well-spread, thin layer, you may have to transfer eggs from the dish in which they were collected into a new container.

3. The active sperm, unlike the eggs, are viable for only a limited time in seawater. Therefore, it is necessary to keep the sperm quiescent by collecting them under "dry" conditions (*i.e.*, in an undiluted suspension). A small portion of the "dry" suspension can be diluted in seawater each time that active sperm are needed.

When an animal has been identified as a male, wipe away excess moisture from among the spines on the aboral surface. Invert the male over a clean, chilled (but dry) Syracuse dish. After several large drops of the white sperm suspension are in the dish, remove the urchin and snugly cover the dish with aluminum foil, parafilm, or some other covering material. The sperm should be kept in this condition until just prior to use when they can be activated by dilution in seawater. At 10°C, the collected sperm may be stored "dry" for several hours, or they may be stored for up to a day in a 5°C refrigerator.

4. Observe suspensions of eggs and sperm microscopically and record your observations. To observe active sperm, add a drop of "dry" sperm to 10 ml of seawater in a small container.

The unfertilized egg of the sea urchin is surrounded by a transparent jelly coat, the refractive index of which is the same as that of seawater. Mix a few drops of India ink with a small quantity of seawater and observe the eggs in this suspension. Since the India ink particles do not penetrate the jelly coat, it should stand as a clear area surrounding the egg.

B. Fertilization

1. The fertilization procedure involves adding an appropriate amount of sperm suspension to the egg suspension. A dilute sperm suspension is prepared by placing *one* drop of the undiluted, or "dry," sperm in a Stender dish containing 10 ml of chilled seawater. Mix with a clean pipette to obtain a uniform milky suspension.

Now, place several drops of washed eggs in a container with about 100 ml of seawater. Then, add *one* drop of the *dilute* sperm suspension just prepared to the eggs. Gently mix the sperm and eggs with a clean pipette.

2. *Immediately* transfer a sample of the suspension of eggs and sperm to a deep well depression slide, filling the depression completely. Apply a cover slip, and observe with a compound microscope. The most conspicuous event is the formation of the fertilization membrane. It is unlikely that you will be able to follow the penetration of the sperm, but the appearance of the fertilization membrane is an outward indication that the union of sperm and egg has occurred.

The fertilization membrane gradually lifts away from the surface of the egg in a blister-like manner. It raises first in the area of sperm penetration and spreads outward around the entire egg. At 10°C, the fertilization membrane separates completely from the egg *within one to two minutes*. The elevation of the fertilization membrane is associated with the breakdown of the cortical granules which are located just below the surface of the egg. The fertilization membrane which is thin and soft at first undergoes a hardening process shortly after its elevation. The translucent hyaline layer which forms at the surface of the egg also develops within a few minutes.

Although these processes are very temperature dependent and their timing is also affected by a number of other variables, table 10-1 shows the approximate sequence of events which follow insemination of eggs at 10°C. Note that several of these processes are not observable with the ordinary light microscope.

TABLE 10-1

FERTILIZATION OF STRONGYLOCENTROTUS PURPURATUS AT 10°C

0 seconds	Insemination
30-40 seconds	Breakdown of cortical granules
35-50 seconds	Initiation of elevation of fertilization membrane (5 to 10 seconds following cortical granule breakdown)
60-70 seconds	Completion of cortical granule breakdown
65-80 seconds	Completion of elevation of fertilization membrane
2 minutes	Hyaline layer formed
5 minutes	Fertilization membrane hardened

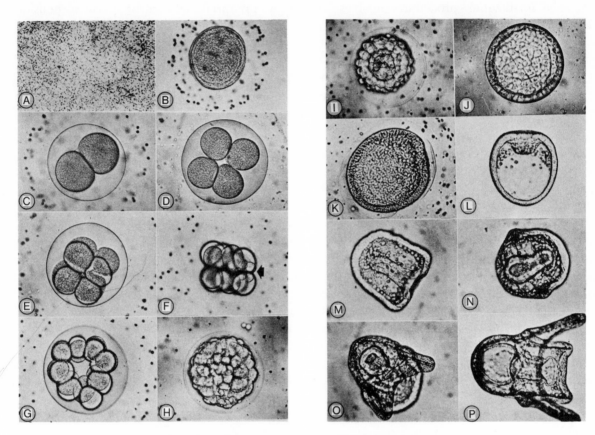

Figure 10-1. Stages in the development of the sand dollar, *Echinorachnius parma*. A. Sperm suspension. B. Unfertilized egg with pigment granules imbedded in the jelly coat. C. Two-cell stage. D. Four-cell stage. E. Eight-cell stage. F. Sixteen-cell stage with the micromeres indicated by and arrow. G. Sixteen-cell stage viewed from a different angle. H. Morula. I. Early blastula. J. Blastula. K. Late blastula at the time of hatching. L. Early gastrula with primary mesenchyme cells visible. M. Late gastrula. N. Prism stage. O. Early pluteus. P. Late pluteus. (Photographs by Dr. D. A. Karnofsky and Miss E. B. Simmel reproduced with the permission of Dr. I. H. Krakoff, Sloan-Kettering Institute for Cancer Research.)

3. Since the fertilization membrane is raised rather quickly, you may wish to use another technique to observe its elevation directly. One means of direct observation consists of placing a drop of eggs and a drop of sperm side-by-side on a microscope slide. With the microscope focused on a group of eggs, the two drops can be connected, or pushed together with a needle. This technique will permit observation of sperm swarming toward the eggs.

Another method, which will permit observation under higher power, involves placing a few grains of sand on a microscope slide so as to leave a space when a cover slip is applied. A drop of unfertilized eggs is placed on the slide and covered with a cover slip. A group of eggs is then brought in clear view under high power. Without disturbing the slide and while focusing on the eggs, a drop of sperm is applied at one edge of the cover slip.

If you can produce dark-field illumination on your microscope, you may wish to repeat one of these techniques using the dark-field technique. There are cortical color changes in the egg which follow sperm contact and you may be able to detect those changes if you are able to observe the eggs during the first 20 or 30 seconds following initial sperm contact. You might also gain additional insights into other aspects of fertilization if you make careful observations with dark-field illumination.

C. Embryonic Development

The embryos of S. *purpuratus* can be raised readily to the early pluteus stage, but are difficult to carry beyond this stage successfully. The embryos should be maintained at temperatures at or below 15°C. If embryos are maintained at about 15°C, each of the developmental stages in the following description will be reached in a shorter time than indicated for observations made on embryos maintained at 10°C. Figure 10-1 is a series of excellent photographs of sand dollar development provided by Karnofsky and Simmel. While some later stages of sea urchin development differ in appearance from the sand dollar, these photos beautifully illustrate salient features of early echinoderm development and will serve as a useful guide for your observations.

Cleavage is equal and holoblastic. The first cleavage, which is meridional, is completed within 3 hours at 10°C. The next division is also meridional. The plane of division in the third cleavage is at right angles to the first two and the product of the division is an 8-celled embryo with an upper quartette of slightly smaller cells and a lower quartette of slightly larger cells. At the fourth cleavage, the 4 blastomeres of the upper, or animal, layer divide equally to form a single tier of 8 medium-sized *mesomeres*. However, the divisions of the 4 vegetal blastomeres are extremely unequal and produce a middle tier of 4 large *macromeres* and a lower tier of 4 very small *micromeres* at the vegetal pole. As cleavage continues the embryo become organized as a single-layered hollow ball of cells surrounding a cavity which is known of the *blastocoel*. The embryo at this stage of development is called a *blastula*.

The embryos hatch at the blastula stage, but even before hatching, rotation of the blastula within the perivitelline space as a result of ciliary activity may be seen. Hatching is accomplished by enzymatic digestion of the membrane and it occurs after about 28 hours of development at 10°C.

After approximately two days (43-48 hours at 10°C), gastrulation may be observed. It is somewhat difficult to see details of gastrulation because of the active movement of embryos during these stages of development, but patient and repeated observations of a number of embryos will permit you to observe at least some of the interesting cellular activities which are involved. After consulting several general descriptions of gastrulation in reference texts, try to observe various aspects of this complex process for yourself. Gastrulation begins with the detachment of the *primary mesenchyme* cells (descendents of the micromeres) from the epithelial blastula wall and their movement into the blastocoel in the vegetal area. Try to observe the pseudopods which these cells extend during the time that they are establishing contacts with other parts of the inner wall of the blastula and moving to new positions in which they will participate in formation of the larval skeleton. The

activities of the primary mesenchyme cells are examples of rather complex individual cell behavior as part of a developmental process. A different set of interpretation problems arises from the in-pushing, or *invagination* of the vegetal area of the blastula. This shape change which is a composite activity of a large number of cells results in the formation of the primitive gut, or *archenteron*, of the embryo. You should be able to observe the stages of this invagination process as it progresses. The *prism* stage, at about 72 hours, represents the transition between the gastrula and the pluteus stages. A major event during the prism stage is the formation of the mouth, an opening made through 2 layers, the endodermal archenteron layer and the ectodermal stomodaeal layer. After 5 days, one may observe the swimming *pluteus,* shaped like a pyramid with four legs. This larval stage was termed "pluteus" because of the similarity which its describer saw to an easel. Observe as much detail of gut structure, skeleton, and other structural aspects of the pluteus larva as time permits.

D. Agglutination and Fertilization

The phenomenon known as sperm agglutination in the sea urchin was first observed by F. R. Lillie, and became the basis for his theory of fertilizin (Lillie, 1923). When unfertilized eggs are removed from the seawater in which they have long been standing, and the supernatant (or "egg water") is then added to a sperm suspension, one observes an instantaneous formation of clusters of sperm. The "egg water" (the supernatant of unfertilized eggs) has the capacity to clump, or *agglutinate,* sperm, and the agglutinating factor in the "egg water" was called "agglutinin" or "fertilizin." Later studies by Tyler showed that the agglutinating factor is present in the jelly layer surrounding mature sea urchin eggs. Whether fertilizin is necessary for fertilization is still debatable. However, the agglutination reaction can be readily observed.

1. The jelly coat surrounding an unfertilized egg will slowly dissolve in seawater. However, to expedite the study, vigorously shake a concentrated sample of unfertilized eggs in 30 ml of seawater in a stoppered test tube. This will aid in removing the jelly coats. Filter this egg suspension and collect the filtrate, or "egg water." Place 3 ml of egg water in a Syracuse dish, or watch glass. Prepare a milky dilute sperm suspension and mix 1 ml of this sperm suspension with the "egg water." Within one minute, the sperm suspension will take on a granular, or flocculent appearance. Microscopically, it may be seen that the sperm are agglutinated in clusters, with the heads of the sperms oriented toward the centers of the clusters.

2. If you wish to study the process of agglutination more closely, place a few grains of sand on a microscope slide. Place a drop of dilute sperm suspension on the slide, and cover with a cover slip. Now, add a drop of "egg water" at the edge of the cover slip. Watch for changes in sperm activity and for the formation of agglutinated masses. According to Lillie, the sperm first become intensely active, or show activation, and then undergo agglutination. Repetition of these observations using dark-field illumination would be instructive.

SUGGESTIONS FOR FURTHER INVESTIGATION

More information on the events of sea urchin fertilization can be found in various texts such as Balinsky (1970) and Berrill (1971) or in more detailed treatments by (Monroy 1965a,b) as well as in many other sources.

Interactions between egg and sperm begin even before the gametes actually contact one another. As you have experimented with one of these interactions, the fertilizin-antifertilizin response, you might find the classical works of Lillie (1913, 1923) of interest for purposes of comparison with modern treatments of the subject. Other interactions which follow the first contact between egg and sperm involve interactions of the egg cell's cortical granules, cell membrane, and vitelline membrane (*e.g.,* see Tegner and Epel, 1973). If you wish to examine these processes in more de-

tail than the coverage afforded by the general references, consult the review of studies on these egg cell responses by Runnström (1966). It is noteworthy that the fertilization membrane may be removed by any of several techniques without adversely affecting further development, (see also Exercise 12), but that experimental modification of the hyaline layer disrupts the normal interaction between blastomeres in early development. For example, it is possible to induce twinning in sea urchin embryos by applying chemical treatments which affect the integrity of the hyaline layer (see Vacquier and Mazia, 1968; Citkowitz, 1971). You might wish to attempt repetition or extension of some of these interesting experiments.

Warburg's discovery in 1908 that sea urchin eggs showed a great increase in oxygen consumption following fertilization led to formation of the hypothesis that activation of respiratory metabolism was a key physiological result of fertilization. Although respiration increases following fertilization are not found universally (egg respiration actually is depressed following fertilization in some organisms), the increase found in sea urchin eggs is an interesting and widely investigated phenomenon. There are a number of types of studies such as metabolic inhibition, temperature alterations, and other treatments which can be done on short term (measured polarographically) or longer term (measured with volumetric respirometry equipment) metabolic responses following fertilization. There are a number of other physiological responses such as greatly increased phosphate uptake which follow fertilization and offer interesting possibilities for experimentation. Consult Balinsky (1970) and Monroy (1965a,b) for access to the literature on these problems. Of course, changes in molecular genetic activity and protein synthesis are critically important aspects of the physiological response to fertilization, but we will defer comment on those topics at this point (see Exercise 12).

Although echinoderm eggs are minute, microsurgical techniques have been applied to the eggs of sea urchins and starfish. There have been a number of studies, notably by Hörstadius, in which blastomeres were separated and recombined in a variety of ways. These experiments contributed importantly to understanding of the physiological differences in various parts of the developing embryo which play roles in normal development. It has been postulated that there are two gradients of physiological activity, one with maximal activity at the animal pole and the other with maximal activity at the vegetal pole, and that normal development depends upon the interaction of the two gradients. You will have an opportunity to explore this concept further in Exercise 12, but some of the details of the experiments on blastomere separation and recombination are given in several of the texts cited in the General References section (*e.g.*, Balinsky, Berrill, Saunders—see also Hörstadius, 1939).

With the increasing sophistication of biologists' understanding of molecular aspects of genetic expression, there is reason to hope that new insights into control of developmental processes at the subcellular level will be gained at an increasing rate in the next few years. On the other end of the developmental spectrum, accurate descriptions of the gross morphological events in development have been available for a number of years. Thus, it would appear that an important gap in understanding can be identified in the area of cellular activity and behavior during morphogenesis (see Trinkaus 1965, 1969). The problem of relating genetic expression and differentiative changes to cell behavior and interaction in developmental processes is being approached in the study of gastrulation in the sea urchin. There are several complex, yet readily observable, changes in cellular activity which apparently involve changes in cell surface properties, cell motility, and cell contractility. These processes are being studied and have been described very lucidly by Gustafson and his co-workers (Gustafson and Wolpert, 1967; Wolpert and Gustafson, 1967; Gustafson and Toneby, 1971).

The diversity of recent studies on sea urchin development is well illustrated in an issue of *Experimental Cell Research* (Vol. 70, No. 1, 1972) which was dedicated to John Runnström.

REFERENCES

GENERAL

BALINSKY, B. I. 1970. *An Introduction to embryology.* 3rd ed. Philadelphia: Saunders.

BERRILL, N. J. 1971. *Developmental biology.* New York: McGraw-Hill.

BODEMER, C. W. 1968. *Modern embryology.* New York: Holt, Rinehart and Winston.

COSTELLO, D. P.; DAVIDSON, M. E.; EGGERS, A.; FOX, M. H.; and HENLEY, C. 1957. *Methods for obtaining and handling marine eggs and embryos.* Woods Hole, Mass.: Marine Biological Laboratory.

EBERT, J. D., and SUSSEX, I. M. 1970. *Interacting systems in development.* 2d ed. New York: Holt, Rinehart and Winston.

GILCHRIST, F. G. 1968. A survey of embryology. New York: McGraw-Hill.

HARVEY, E. B. 1956. *The American Arabacia and other sea urchins.* Princeton, N. J.: Princeton University Press.

HINEGARDNER, R. T. 1967. Echinoderms. In *Methods in developmental biology.* F. H. Wilt and N. K. Wessells eds. New York: Thomas Y. Crowell, pp. 139-155.

SAUNDERS, J. W., JR. 1968. *Patterns and principles of animal development.* New York: Macmillan.

TYLER, A., and TYLER, B. S. 1966. The gametes; some procedures and properties, pp. 639-682, and Physiology of fertilization and early development, pp. 683-741, in *Physiology of Echinodermata.* R. A. Boolootian, ed. New York: Interscience Publishers.

SPECIFIC

CITKOWITZ, E. 1971. The hyaline layer: its isolation and role in echinoderm development. *Develop. Biol.* 24:348-362.

GUSTAFSON, T., and TONEBY, M. I. 1971. How genes control morphogenesis. *American Scientist* 59:452-462.

GUSTAFSON, T., and WOLPERT, L. 1967. Cellular movement and contact in sea urchin morphogenesis. *Biol. Rev.* 42:442-498.

HÖRSTADIUS, S. 1939. The mechanics of sea urchin development, studied by operative methods. *Biol. Rev.* 14:132-179.

LILLIE, F. R. 1913. The mechanism of fertilization. *Science* 38:524-528. (Reprinted in *Foundations of experimental embryology*, B. H. Willier and J. M. Oppenheimer eds. Englewood Cliffs, N. J.: Prentice-Hall, 1964).

———. 1923. *Problems of Fertilization.* Chicago: University of Chicago Press.

MONROY, A. 1965a. Biochemical aspects of fertilization. In *The biochemisetry of animal development,* (Vol. 1), R. Weber ed. New York: Academic Press.

———. 1965b. *Chemistry and physiology of fertilization.* New York: Holt, Rinehart and Winston.

RUNNSTRÖM, J. 1966. The vitelline membrane and cortical particles in sea urchin eggs and their function in maturation and fertilization. *Advances in Morphogenesis* 5:221-325.

TEGNER, M. J., and EPEL, D. 1973. Sea urchin sperm-egg interactions studied with the scanning electron microscope. *Science* 179:685-688.

TRINKAUS, J. P. 1965. Mechanisms of morphogenetic movements. In *Organogenesis,* R. L. DeHaan and H. Ursprung eds. New York: Holt, Rinehart and Winston, pp. 55-104.

———. 1969. *Cells into organs. The forces that shape the embryo.* Englewood Cliffs, N. J.: Prentice-Hall.

VACQUIER, V. D., and MAZIA, D. 1968. Twinning of sea urchin embryos by treatment with dithiothreitol. Roles of cell surface interactions and of the hyaline layer. *Exp. Cell Res.* 52:459-468.

WARBURG, O. 1908. Observations on oxidative processes in the sea urchin egg. *Hoppe-Seyler's Zeits. f. physiol. Chem.* 57:1-16. (Translated and reprinted in *Foundations of Experimental Embryology*, B. H. Willier and J. M. Oppenheimer eds. Englewood Cliffs, N. J.: Prentice-Hall, 1964).

WOLPERT, L., and GUSTAFSON, T. 1967. Cell movement and cell contact in sea urchin morphogenesis. *Endeavour* 26:85-90.

MATERIALS

EQUIPMENT

Syracuse dishes
Finger bowls
Stender dishes or very small (1 1/2 inch) finger bowls
Beakers
Clean syringes and hypodermic needles
Clean disposable Pasteur pipettes
Aluminum foil or parafilm
Miscroscope slides and cover slips
Compound microscope
Dark field stop for microscope, if available
India ink
Depression slide
Test tube with stopper
Filter paper and funnel

SOLUTIONS AND CHEMICALS

Cold seawater or appropriate salt mixture ("artificial seawater")
0.5 M KCl solution
Washed fine sand

LIVING MATERIAL

Purple sea urchins (*Strongylocentrotus purpuratus*)or other sea urchins, if desired or necessary

Organization of the Sea Urchin Egg

Experimental work on sea urchin eggs began with Driesch's pioneering studies in the 1890's which revealed that isolated blastomeres of the 2-cell (or 4-cell) stage give rise to normally proportioned, though undersized, larvae. Each blastomere has the capability to develop into a whole embryo. However, if the sea urchin egg is cut in half through the equator after the equatorial third cleavage, the animal and vegetal halves show distinctly different developmental capacities. The animal half develops into a hollow ball of ciliated cells (a "dauerblastula") while the vegetal half develops into a partial larva containing a digestive tube of endodermal origin and skeletal components of mesodermal origin. Evidently, cells of the animal hemisphere are determined for differentiation along ectodermal lines and those of the vegetal hemisphere for differentiation along endodermal and mesodermal pathways.

Experiments conducted by Hörstadius and other workers in the 1930s led to the formulation of the "double-gradient" theory of differentiation in the sea urchin. This theory proposes that within the developing egg there are two antagonistic factors or physiological activities which interact to produce normal development and that each of these factors displays a gradient of intensity associated with specific areas of the egg. The intensity of one factor or activity is maximal at the animal pole and promotes the development of ectodermal tissue. The other is maximal at the vegetal pole and promotes the development of endodermal tissues. Normal development depends upon the proper interaction of the two gradients, where neither gradient overrides the effects of the other. If one of the gradients is depressed, the embryo develops under the influence of the other prevailing gradient. Thus, the predominance of animal hemisphere cells (as a result of the removal of vegetal cells, for example) leads to "animalization" of the embryo. The embryo becomes solely an ectodermal ball with an excessive complement of cilia. The digestive system or skeletal parts

161

never form. Conversely, a disproportionate reduction of animal hemisphere cells results in "vegetali-zation" of the embryo. Since the presumptive endoderm is excessive in comparison to the ectoderm, invagination becomes impossible. Thus, the endoderm fails to move to the interior and the archen-teron is turned inside out (an "exogastrula"). In such cases, the ectodermal derivatives are reduced to a thin-walled "umbrella."

The intensity of the respective gradients can be altered by "defect" and "transplantation" experiments—*i.e.*, the removal of blastomere groups, or the transplantation of bastomeres—or by chemical means. As we shall see in this exercise, anomalies of development can result from various chemicals which change the intensity of the gradients.

This exercise will introduce you to a few ways that the sea urchin egg can be manipulated to provide some insight into its organization and patterns of differentiation. One of these experiments relates to the gradient hypothesis while the others, artificial parthenogenetic activation and the de-velopment of isolated early blastomeres, reveal other aspects of the organization and developmental capacities of the sea urchin egg.

TECHNIQUES

A. Development of a Whole Embryo from an Isolated Blastomere

The technique to be described dates back to Driesch in 1892, who literally shook apart the blastomeres of the sea urchin embryo in the early cleavage stages and followed the development of the individual blastomeres. It takes advantage of the fact that the fertilization membrane is fragile immediately after fertilization and, hence, can be removed by shaking the egg. Without a hardened fertilization membrane, the cells of the 2-cell stage subsequently can be separated.

1. Obtain eggs as described in the preceding exercise (Exercise 10). Place a sample of eggs in a test tube half-full of seawater, introduce one drop of dilute sperm suspension into the tube and seal the tube with a rubber stopper. Aid the mixing of sperm and eggs by inverting the tube once.

2. Exactly *one* minute after introducing the sperm, vigorously shake the tube without inter-ruption for a full *two* minutes. A relatively large number of fertilization membranes should be ruptured by the violent shaking.

3. Transfer the contents of the tube to a Stender dish and, after 1 hour, examine the eggs for indications of the onset of first cleavage. Continue to make observations at periodic intervals until the first cleavage division has just been completed. With a clean pipette, squirt several strong jets of seawater into the culture. Allow the eggs to settle and check microscopically for separated blas-tomere pairs.

Separation can also be brought about by again vigorously shaking the eggs in a test tube, but the percentage return is not as great as subjecting the eggs to strong jets of seawater. If neither technique is successfull in your hands, you might try Herbst's method of placing the eggs which are undergoing the first division in artificial seawater from which calcium salts have been omitted. When left in calcium-free seawater until the completion of the first division, the blastomeres will separate when squirted with jets of seawater. Once isolated, however, the blastomeres must be re-turned to normal seawater.

4. Transfer the isolated blastomeres to a finger bowl of seawater, cover the bowl, and observe development to the pluteus stage in subsequent days.

Compare the relative sizes of normal plutei and "half-embryo" plutei.

B. Exogastrulation

Different chemical agents have been found to bring about either "animalization" or "vegetalization" of the sea urchin embryo. Exposure of the early embryo to lithium salts results in vegetalization, with the consequent formation of an exogastrula. In later stages of development, however, lithium has no observable detrimental effects.

1. If the LiCl solutions have not been prepared in advance, use seawater and a stock solution of 0.5 M LiCl to prepare the following solutions:

   a. 0.03 M LiCl (94 parts seawater plus 6 parts 0.5 M LiCl)
   b. 0.025 M LiCl (95 parts seawater plus 5 parts 0.5 M LiCl)
   c. 0.02 M LiCl (96 parts seawater plus 4 parts 0.5 M LiCl)
   d. 0.015 M LiCl (97 parts seawater plus 3 parts 0.5 M LiCl)

Use seawater or your artificial seawater solution as a control medium.

2. Inseminate eggs as previously described in Exercise 10. Add samples of eggs to each of the lithium chloride solutions in Syracuse dishes or other culture vessels at the following intervals: (a) 4 hours post-fertilization, (b) 24 hours post-fertilization, and (c) 36 hours post-fertilization. Record your observations of further development and watch for signs of exogastrulation. Compare developmental patterns and rates in the various groups with normal development observed in seawater.

C. Artificial Parthenogenesis

The sea urchin has the capacity to begin development parthenogenetically. It is very susceptible to the action of external agents, and several substances have been shown to induce parthenogenetic development. Loeb showed that various concentrations of electrolytes such as $MgCl_2$ and KCl, and non-electrolytes such as cane sugar and urea, induce cleavage of the sea urchin egg. He also found that eggs in hypertonic seawater underwent mitotic divisions. In the experiment below, hypertonic seawater will be used as the parthenogenetic agent.

1. Various concentrations of hypertonic artificial seawater solutions can be prepared directly; or, if you actually are using seawater, you can concentrate the solution by boiling off enough water to reduce the volume appropriately. Test the effectiveness of 1.5X, 2X, and 4X normal concentration artificial seawater solution or seawater using a standard exposure time of 5 minutes.

2. Transfer samples of washed, unfertilized eggs to each of three stender dishes containing the three different concentrations of hypertonic seawater. After 5 minutes of treatment, decant the hypertonic seawater and wash the eggs with three changes of normal seawater.

3. After the eggs have been thoroughly washed, examine them for the presence of fertilization membranes. The membranes of parthenogenetically activated eggs lift off more slowly than those of normally inseminated eggs. If typical membranes are produced, check later for evidences of cleavage and even further development. Determine the stage of developmental arrest in the parthenogenetically activated eggs.

SUGGESTIONS FOR FURTHER INVESTIGATION

Dreisch's early experiments on separation of sea-urchin blastomeres can be thought of as the historical beginning of several lines of investigation. His experiments demonstrated that early cleavage cells of the sea urchin could "regulate" to develop complete, but undersized, larvae. This demonstration was of historical importance because it was the first of a series of comparative studies which categorized developmental patterns in various organisms on the basis of the developmental potential of the early blastomeres (see Balinsky, 1970). In the modern, cellular context, his work could be cited as the first evidence supporting the hypothesis that cell divisions during develop-

ment involve full and complete replication of nuclear genetic information. You might enjoy reading some of Dreisch's contributions (Dreisch, 1892) and the interesting comments about Dreisch and his intellectual development which are included in Willier and Oppenheimer (1964).

Hörstadius (1939) and other workers demonstrated the developmental fates of various experimentally contrived combinations of early cleavage cells. The analysis of results of various combinations of cells from the 16-cell stage was particularly instrumental in establishment of the double gradient hypothesis of developmental control in the sea urchin. Balinsky (1970) reviews these results succinctly and information on them is also available in Berrill (1971) and Saunders (1968). Balinsky also surveys chemical modification of the gradients, but you may want to consult more detailed treatments such as those by Lallier (1964) or Gustafson (1965). Animalizing and vegetalizing substances have actually been extracted and isolated from unfertilized eggs themselves by Josefsson and Hörstadius (1969).

As you experimented with a vegetalizing agent in this exercise, you might wish to study the action of an animalizing substance. The dye Evans Blue is regarded as a very reliable animalizing agent in the cases of many sea urchins (e.g., O'Melia, 1971). Evans Blue is effective even at very low concentrations. You could test the influence of several concentrations and the effects of exposure to Evans Blue during various phases of development by transferring embryos to Evans Blue solutions at various times beginning with the 2-cell stage. Possibly a fairly broad range of concentrations centered around 1/25,000 Evans Blue in seawater would give you an initial range of test possibilities. See O'Melia (1973) for more recent references to this work.

Artificial parthenogenesis in sea urchin eggs has been studied for many years. From the time that the Hertwigs discovered that treatment with chloroform or strychnine would cause development of ripe sea urchin eggs to proceed, eggs have been subjected to a variety of rude treatments, many of which have proven to be more or less effective as parthenogenetic agents. The common factor in most of these treatments seems to be that they slightly damage the egg, but the list of effective agents includes such a variety of chemical and physical treatments that it is difficult to make any other generalization about them. Some of the early studies on artificial parthenogenesis are described in the classical book by Loeb (1913). Consult Harvey (1956) and Balinsky (1970) for further information.

Sea urchin eggs have been favored for biochemical studies on genetic expression in early development because of the regularity of their developmental patterns and the ease with which fairly large amounts of material at a single stage of development can be obtained for biochemical analysis. While a survey of this extensive work is impossible in the space available, an additional example of the importance of egg organization at the biochemical level can be derived from these studies.

One of the striking biochemical events associated with the fertilization of the sea urchin egg is a marked increase in protein synthesis. It would be tempting to suggest that the messenger RNA which directs the assembly of these protein molecules is lacking in the unfertilized sea urchin egg and that fertilization triggers the synthesis of large quantities of messenger RNA. This suggestion is not supported by experimental evidence because several studies (e.g. Gross, Malkin, and Moyer, 1964) have indicated that the normal post-fertilization increase in protein synthesis can occur even when transcription of nuclear genetic information is prevented such as is the case when eggs are pretreated with Actinomycin D. In fact, fragments of sea urchin eggs lacking nuclei show an increase in protein synthesis upon activation with artificial parthenogenetic agents which closely parallels that seen if similar fragments are fertilized with normal sperm (Denny and Tyler, 1964). Thus, the initial increase in protein synthesis can occur in the absence of nuclear material. It is quite generally accepted that the messenger RNA (and other classes of RNA as well) needed to direct early protein synthesis is present in the cytoplasm of the mature sea urchin egg (see also Humphreys, 1971). This example emphasizes, once again, the importance of egg organization for control of early development. It should be noted that new RNA synthesis becomes essential during late cleavage or

early gastrulation stages, and that if it is prevented, development will not proceed normally. A large percentage of current issues of journals in the field of Developmental Biology contain papers on these and related topics, but you might wish to do further background reading in more general sources. General treatments of biochemical aspects of genetic activity as well as citations of relevant review articles are available in Balinsky (1970) and Berrill (1971). Additional details and more extensive literature citations can be found in more specialized sources such as Ebert and Sussex (1970), Davidson (1968), or Markert and Ursprung (1971).

If it is possible for you to experiment with the effects of Actinomycin D on sea urchin development, you should consult Greenhouse, Hynes, and Gross (1971) and, possibly, Summers (1970) before you begin your work. However, Actinomycin D is quite expensive and another type of approach might be required. Another agent which interferes with nucleic acid metabolism and causes morphologically detectable abnormalities in the development of some sea urchins is the acridine, ethidium bromide (Brachet, 1968). At lower concentrations, the results of ethidium bromide treatment applied continuously from early cleavage onward resemble those induced by Actinomycin D because 15 µg/ml blocks development of *Paracentratus lividus* at early gastrulation (Vacquier and Claybrook, 1969). If embryos are transferred to ethidium bromide solutions at early gastrula stages, the formation of skeletal spicules is abnormal. Higher concentrations (20-30 µg/ml) stop cleavage and induce mitotic abnormalities (Vacquier and Brachet, 1969).

REFERENCES

GENERAL

BALINSKY, B. I. 1970. *An introduction to embryology.* 3rd ed. Philadelphia: Saunders.

BERRILL, N. J. 1971. *Developmental biology.* New York: McGraw-Hill.

HARVEY, E. B. 1956. *The American Arbacia and other sea urchins.* Princeton, N. J.: Princeton University Press.

SAUNDERS, J. W. JR. 1968. *Patterns and principles of animal development.* New York: Macmillan.

SPECIFIC

BRACHET, J. 1968. Effects of acridines on morphogenesis. *Nature* 220:488-489.

DAVIDSON, E. H. 1968. *Gene activity in early development.* New York: Academic Press.

DENNY, P. C., and TYLER A. 1964. Activation of protein biosynthesis in non-nucleate fragments of sea urchin eggs. *Biochem. Biophys. Res. Comm.* 14:245-249. (Also reprinted in *Developmental biology*, R. A. Flickinger ed. Dubuque, Iowa: Wm. C. Brown Company Publishers, 1966).

DREISCH, H. 1892. The potency of the first two cleavage cells in echinoderm development. Experimental production of partial and double formations. *Zeit. f. wiss. Zool.* 53:160-178; 183-184. (Abridged, translated and reprinted in *Foundations of experimental embryology*, B. H. Willier and J. M. Oppenheimer eds. Englewood Cliffs, N. J.: Prentice-Hall, 1964).

EBERT, J. D., and SUSSEX, I. M. 1970. *Interacting systems in development.* 2d ed. New York: Holt, Rinehart and Winston.

GREENHOUSE, G. A.; HYNES, R. O.; and GROSS, P. R. 1971. Sea urchin embryos are permeable to actinomycin. *Science* 171:686-689.

GROSS, P. R.; MALKIN, L. I.; and MOYER, W. A. 1964. Templates for the first proteins of embryonic development. *Proc. Nat. Acad. Sci.* 51:407-414. (Also reprinted in *Developmental biology*, R. A. Flickinger ed. Dubuque, Iowa: Wm. C. Brown Company Publishers, 1966).

GUSTAFSON, T. 1965. Morphogenetic significance of biochemical patterns in sea urchin embryos. In *Biochemistry of animal development*, Vol. I, R. Weber ed. New York: Academic Press.

HÖRSTADIUS, S. 1939. The mechanics of sea urchin development, studied by operative methods. *Biol. Rev.* 14:132-179.

HUMPHREYS, T. 1971. Measurements of messenger RNA entering polysomes upon fertilization of sea urchin eggs. *Develop. Biol.* 26:201-208.

169

Josefsson, L., and Hörstadius, S. 1969. Morphogenetic substances from sea urchin eggs. Isolation of animalizing and vegetalizing substances from unfertilized eggs of *Paracentrotus lividus. Develop. Biol.* 20:481-500.

Lallier, R. 1964. Biochemical aspects of animalization and vegetalization in the sea urchin embryo. *Advances in Morphogenesis* 3: 147-196.

Loeb, J. 1913. *Artificial parthenogenesis and fertilization.* Chicago: University of Chicago Press.

Markert, C. L., and Ursprung, H. 1971. *Developmental genetics.* Englewood Cliffs, N. J.: Prentice-Hall.

O'Melia, A. F. 1971. Animalizing effect of Evans Blue in embryos of *Arbacia punctulata. Exp. Cell Res.* 67:402-406.

———. 1973. Animalizing effect of Evans Blue in embryos of *Arbacia punctulata.* Effect on multiple molecular forms of NAD-ℓ-Malate Dehydrogenase. *Exp. Cell Res.* 77:280-284.

Summers, R. G. 1970. The effect of actinomycin D on demembranated *Lytechinus variegatus* embryos. *Exp. Cell Res.* 59:170-171.

Vacquier, V. D., and Brachet, J. 1969. Chromosomal abnormalities resulting from ethidium bromide treatment. *Nature* 222:193-195.

Vacquier, V. D., and Claybrook, J. R. 1969. Biochemical consequences of ethidium bromide treatment of sea urchin embryos. *Nature* 224:706-707.

MATERIALS

Equipment
Syracuse dishes
Finger bowls
Stender dishes or very small finger bowls (1 1/2 inch)
Beakers
Clean syringes and hypodermic needles
Clean disposable Pasteur pipettes
Aluminum foil or parafilm
Microscope slides and cover slips
Depression slide
Compound microscope
Test tube with stopper

Solutions and Chemicals
Cold seawater or appropriate salt mixture ("artificial seawater")
1.5 X normal concentration seawater
2 X normal concentration seawater
4 X normal concentration seawater
0.5 M KCl solution
0.5 M LiCl solution for preparation of various LiCl solutions required in section B.

Living Material
Purple sea urchins (*Strongylocentrotus purpuratus*) or other sea urchins, if desired or necessary.

Cell Proliferation and Specialization During Sea Urchin Cleavage

Cleavage is a period during which repeated mitotic divisions convert the relatively large egg cell into a multicellular embryo which will carry on further development. The mitotic divisions of cleavage differ from mitosis in most other situations because the cell cycle during cleavage does not include growth in cell size. In fact, cleavage involves a progressive decrease in cell size. During cleavage, cellular activity appears to be concentrated on the processes of cell proliferation and only after the rate of multiplication slows does other cellular activity such as structural rearrangement by orderly cell movement become apparent. Thus, cleavage is a distinctive period of development characterized by increase in cell numbers due to repeated mitotic divisions, and its end is marked by a decline in the rate of cell division and the initiation of other developmental activities.

One characteristic feature of cleavage is that specialized areas of egg cytoplasm (especially the egg cortex) are not displaced from their original positions relative to one another. They simply are isolated as cytoplasmic components of the various cleavage cells in their respective areas of the cleaving egg. Thus, biochemical specializations of areas of egg cytoplasm (see Exercise 11) are perpetuated as biochemical specializations of cleavage cells in specific areas. While biochemical specialization cannot be visualized directly, it is possible to see morphological evidence of cell specialization even during early cleavage stages in the sea urchin. For example, recall (see also Exercise 10) that the first 2 cleavages in the sea urchin are meridional and equal and that they produce 4 equal-size blastomeres. The third cleavage divisions produce 4 slightly smaller cells above 4 slightly larger cells. Then during the fourth cleavage, very unequal cytoplasmic divisions in the vegetal area produce the 4 large macromeres and 4 very small micromeres while equal cytoplasmic divisions in the animal region produce the 8 mesomeres. Recognizable differences in cell size are perpetuated throughout early development. Later, descendants of these special groups of cells proceed to very different developmental fates.

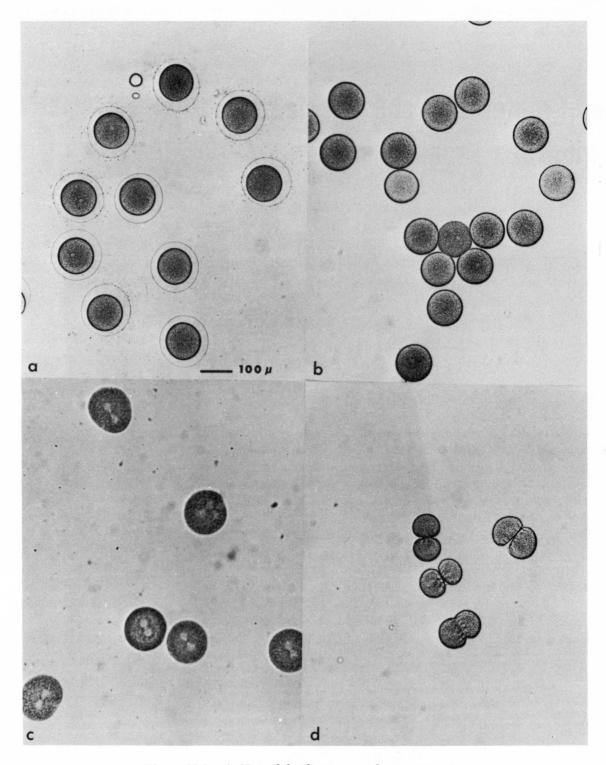

Figure 12-1. A. Normal fertilization membranes present on *Lytechinus pictus* eggs. B. eggs from which fertilization membranes have been removed by gentle homogenization. C. Demembraned eggs approaching the first cleavage division. D. The end of the first cleavage division in membrane-free eggs. (Photographs provided by Dr. B. R. Burchill, University of Kansas).

In addition to introducing additional techniques used in experimentation on sea urchin eggs, this brief exercise is intended to permit you to study quantitatively patterns of cell proliferation during sea urchin cleavage and to observe the more easily visible evidences of early cell specialization. The exercise utilizes a combination of the the technique of Burchill and Blomquist (1969) for fertilization membrane removal and that of Hinegardner (1967) for examination of individual cells.

TECHNIQUES

A. Removal of the Fertilization Membrane

The eggs of the West Coast purple sea urchin, *Strongylocentrotus purpuratus*, are to be fertilized according to procedures described in Exercise 10. The study of the individual cleaving cells necessitates that the fertilization membrane be removed. There are several methods for eliminating the fertilization membrane, but we shall employ a technique reported by Burchill and Blomquist (1969). Eggs (of the sea urchin *Lytechinus pictus*) were demembraned in glass homogenizers. Figure 12-1, reproduced from Burchill and Blomquist's manuscript, shows homogenized eggs after removal of the membrane. One advantage of the technique is that it does not require the addition of any chemicals to the medium as is the case with several other techniques for fertilization membrane removal.

1. As soon as the fertilization membrane has appeared (within 1 minute after insemination), centrifuge the eggs gently for a few seconds (5-10 sec.) to separate them from the sperm-containing seawater. Immediately pour off the supernatant seawater, and re-suspend the eggs in fresh seawater. Pour the egg suspension into a glass homogenizer. With gentle pressure, slowly force a Teflon pestle (with a clearance rating of 0.004-0.006 inches) through the suspension, and then slowly withdraw the pestle.

2. Examine a sample of eggs microscopically. If the treatment was completed within 4 minutes following insemination, very few eggs should have retained intact membranes. The fertilization membranes harden by about 5 minutes after insemination, and are no longer easily removed. Thus, except for the slow, meticulous handling of the pestle, you should work with appreciable speed.

3. Demembraned eggs must be handled very gently. Permit the homogenized eggs to settle by gravity, pour off the supernatant containing the membranes, and re-suspend the eggs in regular seawater.

B. Examination and Counting of Cells

Hinegardner (1967) presents a relatively simple procedure for examining and counting the number of cells in the demembraned, pre-hatching embryo.

1. Add *one* drop of demembraned eggs in seawater to 10 drops of 0.001 M EDTA in 1.5 M dextrose solution. Allow the embryos to remain in this solution for ten minutes. This length of time is a good initial choice, but the necessary duration of treatment varies with the developmental stage, and some trial-and-error will be necessary in determining the appropriate duration of treatment. If the treatment is excessively long, the cells will tend to fall apart before they are transferred to a slide for observation. Too brief treatment will result in difficulty in dispersing the cells after transfer.

2. Transfer several drops of eggs, suspended in the dextrose medium, to a microscope slide. Add a cover slip and then blot around the edges of the cover slip with blotting paper. Flow caused by blotting will tend to flatten the embryos, as well as to cause the cells to spread out into monolayered streaks. Examine the slide microscopically. In some cases, it may be necessary to move the cover slip sideways a millimeter or two to produce a well spread streak of cells.

175

3. For embryos in a given developmental period, count the cells in several of the "streaked" embryos. Prepare an average of several counts and plot the average number of cells against time after fertilization. Try to determine the pattern of cell proliferation with time during cleavage and to detect the decline in division rate at the end of cleavage.

Take particular note of the different kinds of cells that comprise the pre-hatching embryo and try to determine whether there is a continuous range of size variation among the cells at various stages or there are definite cell size classes.

SUGGESTIONS FOR FURTHER INVESTIGATION

General information on cleavage and references to descriptive and experimental studies on cleavage in sea urchins and other organisms can be obtained from the texts listed in the General References section.

For many different types of investigations, the tough fertilization membrane of the echinoderm egg must be removed. Numerous techniques involving physical manipulation, chemical treatment, or even osmotic means have been devised to eliminate the membrane. You have been introduced to a convenient method in this exercise (see also Exercise 11), but you may wish to try other procedures for purposes of comparison or in experiments suggested in other exercises on sea urchin development. Lindahl and Lundin (1948) passed fertilized eggs through bolting silk under pressure. The size of the mesh was slightly less than the diameter of the eggs. The treatment requires carefully constructed apparatus and rigorous attention to technique. Exacting pressure regulation is necessary since excessively high pressure breaks a large percentage of the eggs while low pressure leaves most membranes intact. Tyler and Spiegel (1956) fertilized sea urchin eggs in seawater containing papain and cysteine. The fertilization membranes dissolved in this medium, and the demembraned eggs were separated from the added substances by centrifugation. To prevent hardening of the fertilization membrane, Mazia *et al.* (1961) transferred fertilized eggs, within 30 seconds after insemination, into a mercaptoethylgluconamide—and versene—containing solution. Fifteen minutes later, the eggs were passed through bolting silk to remove the membranes which do not harden in this medium. Additional suggestions of techniques for handling and experimenting with early echinoderm embryos can be found in the reviews of Hinegardner (1967) and Berg (1967).

Studies of the developmental significance of the different size classes of cells in the various areas of the early sea urchin embryo have a long history (see Exercises 10 and 11). More recently, biochemical analysis of some properties of the various groups of cells at the sixteen-cell stage has become possible because of development of techniques for separating and collecting cells of different sizes. Hynes and Gross (1970) dissociated cells of demembraned embryos in calcium- and magnesium-free seawater, layered them over Ficoll density gradients and centrifuged them briefly. They were able to recover quite homogeneous batches of cells of different sizes from specific hands in the gradients (see also Spiegel and Tyler, 1966).

177

REFERENCES

GENERAL

BALINSKY, B. I. 1970. *An introduction to embryology.* 3rd ed. Philadelphia: Saunders.

BERG, W. E. 1967. Some experimental techniques for eggs and embryos of marine invertebrates. In *Methods in developmental biology,* F. H. Wilt and N. K. Wessells eds. New York: Thomas Y. Crowell, pp. 767-776.

BERRILL, N. J. 1971. *Developmental biology.* New York: McGraw-Hill.

EBERT, J. D., and SUSSEX, I. M. 1970. *Interacting systems in development.* 2d ed. New York: Holt, Rinehart and Winston.

HINEGARDNER, R. T. 1967. Echinoderms. In *Methods in developmental biology,* F. H. Wilt and N. K. Wessells eds. New York: Thomas Y. Crowell, pp. 139-155.

SAUNDERS, J. W., JR. 1968. *Patterns and principles of animal development.* New York: Macmillan.

SPECIFIC

BURCHILL, B. R., and BLOMQUIST, C. H. 1969. Removal of fertilization membranes from sea urchin (*Lytechinus pictus*) eggs. *Experientia* 25:540-541.

LINDAHL, P. E., and LUNDIN, J. 1948. Removal of the fertilization membranes from large quantities of sea urchin eggs. *Science* 108:481-482.

HYNES, R. O., and GROSS, P. R. 1970. A method for separating cells from early sea urchin embryos. *Develop. Biol.* 21:383-402.

MAZIA, D.; MITCHISON, J. M.; MEDINA H.; and HARRIS, P. 1961. The direct isolation of the mitotic apparatus. *Jour. Biophys. Biochem. Cytol.* 10:467-474.

SPIEGEL, M., and TYLER, A. 1966. Protein synthesis in micromeres of the sea urchin egg. *Science* 151:1233-1234.

TYLER, A., and SPIEGEL, M. 1956. Elevation and retraction of the fertilization membrane of echinoderm eggs fertilized in papain solutions. *Biol. Bull.* 10:196-200.

MATERIALS

EQUIPMENT

Syracuse dishes

Finger bowls

Stender dishes or very small (1 1/2 inch) finger bowls

Beakers

Clean syringes and hypodermic needles

Clean disposable Pasteur pipettes

Aluminum foil or parafilm

Microscope slides and cover slips

Compound microscope

Clinical or hand centrifuge with tubes

Glass homogenizer and teflon pestle with clearance rating of 0.004-0.006 inches (e.g. Tri-R model S21 or S35)

Blotting (bibulous) paper

SOLUTIONS AND CHEMICALS

Cold seawater or appropriate salt mixture ("artificial seawater")

0.5 M KCl solution

0.001 M EDTA (versene) in 1.5 M dextrose solution

LIVING MATERIAL

Purple sea urchins (*Strongylocentrotus purpuratus*) or other sea urchins if desired or necessary.

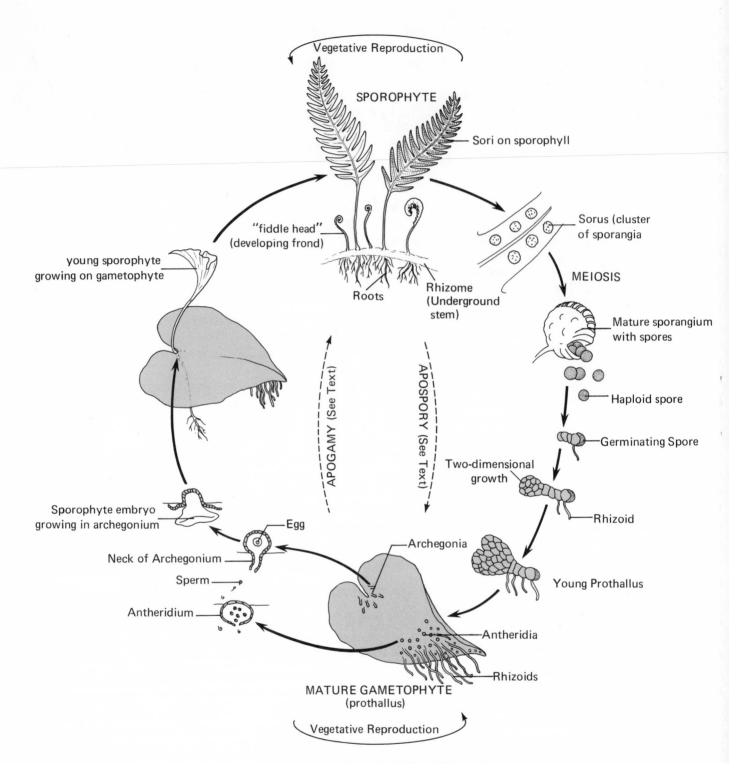

Figure 13-1. Generalized fern life cycle.

Patterns of Fern Gametophyte Development

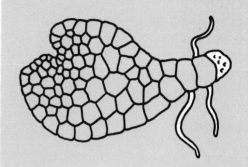

The *gametophyte* (gamete-producing plant) of the bracken fern, *Pteridium aquilinum,* grows well under laboratory culture conditions, and the early stages of its development can be traced by direct microscopic observation following transfer of spores to a suitable medium. This direct observation makes it possible to assess readily the morphological effects of experimental treatments. Problems of fern gametophyte development have attracted the attention of a number of developmental biologists.

You should review the major features of the life cycle of the fern. A simplified, diagrammatic outline of the life history of a typical fern is represented in Figure 13-1. The *sporophyte,* or spore-producing phase of the fern life history, is the familiar "fern plant" seen growing both in gardens and in the wild. The fern *gametophyte* is a relatively inconspicuous, independent plant, the *prothallus,* upon which develop *antheridia* (sperm-producing organs) and *archegonia* (egg-producing organs). In the case of *Pteridium aquilinum,* both types of reproductive organs are borne on the same prothallus, but antheridia are produced before archegonia on a given prothallus.

This exercise is primarily a description of the development of the gametophyte phase of the fern's life cycle. However, if you are able to maintain your cultures for a relatively long period, you will have the opportunity to observe the young sporophytes.

TECHNIQUES

A. Preparation of Cultures

Directions for growing fern gametophytes from spores are included, but your instructor may elect to start the cultures in advance of the first laboratory period.

1. A mixture of inorganic salts has been found by Davis and Postlethwait (1966) to support the growth of the fern gametophyte.

The composition of the culture medium is shown in Appendix F. After the liquid medium has been prepared, fill culture dishes (either petri dishes or Erlenmeyer flasks) about half full. Mark the fluid level on the outside of the dish so that you can add distilled water to the dishes later if evaporation occurs. It is best to position the culture dishes where the plants are to be grown before spores are added. This eliminates handling which tends to wash spores up on the edges of the dishes where they dry out or develop poorly. Sprinkle a very lightly scattered layer of spores on the surface of the medium. Do *not* cover the surface with a dense mat of spores since overcrowding inhibits development. If dishes *must* be handled after seeding, move them carefully with a minimum amount of disturbance of the growth medium. If flasks are used, they must be stoppered with cotton plugs or covered with aluminum foil.

2. Cultures should be kept in an area which receives a moderate amount of light during the day. A north-facing window ledge would be one possible site or "soft white," fluorescent, desk-lamp bulbs can be used to provide artificial light. A desk lamp with two 15-watt bulbs set at a height of 10 to 12 inches above the culture supports good development if the lights are on for at least 8 to 10 hours per day. The bright light conditions of sunny, south-facing windows and certain types of "growth chambers" should be avoided.

3. Your culture can be maintained indefinitely and usually requires only occasional checks on fluid level. Contamination should not be a serious problem on this medium, but if some areas become contaminated, attempt to "rescue" plants from other parts of the culture and transfer them to fresh culture dishes.

4. Remove plants from your culture for observation at intervals. As you probably will have an excess of material, don't attempt to return plants to the culture after observation. During early development, you can transfer plants to a slide for observation using either a bacteriological loop or a pipette. As growth continues, it may become necessary to handle prothallia gently with a spatula and a forceps. Place material in a drop of water on the slide, cover it with a cover slip, and make observations under the low power objective of a compound microscope.

OBSERVATIONS

Your observations should be made critically and recorded carefully as they will constitute the normal, "control" developmental pattern against which you will base comparisons in the next two experimental exercises.

1. Check your cultures at daily intervals. When you find germinating spores, begin to record pertinent facts about early development such as the approximate percentage of germination, the sequence of appearance and characteristics of the first cell of the *protonema* (the filamentous chain of cells which will grow out from the spore) and the first *rhizoid* (see Fig. 13-2A).

2. A critically important step in the early development of the gametophyte is an abrupt alteration in growth form. Early growth takes the form of a protonemal chain of cells lying end to end ("one-dimentional growth"). After a few days under ordinary white-light conditions, the plane of cell division at the end of the filament is reoriented so that two daughter cells produced by a division come to lie side-by-side at oblique angles to the linear chain of earlier cells. The change in division pattern marks the beginning of the flat, plate-like gametophyte prothallus ("two-dimensional growth"). (See Fig. 13-2B). Record the time sequence of this transition in your culture and note the number of protonema cells present at the time of conversion from one-dimensional growth to two-dimensional growth.

3. As you follow development of the young gametophyte, make sketches to record its general appearance at various stages. Quantitative data are also relatively easy to obtain and should be recorded. As most areas of the gametophyte are only one cell thick, it is possible to obtain reasonably accurate counts of total cell number. Plot these data against time as you go along so that you have a reference curve for cell proliferation under your culture conditions. You will encounter considerable individual variability, but your results should still be representative of the general sequence of events in prothallus development.

A.

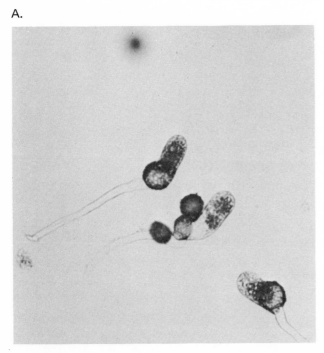

B.

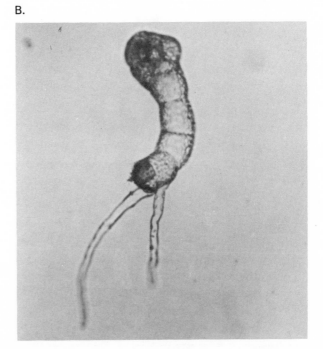

Figure 13-2. A. One dimensional gametophytes with rhizoids growing out of germinated spores. B. Early two-dimensional gametophyte. C. Heart-shaped prothallus showing distinct apical notch. D. Enlargement of a portion of prothallus showing several antheridia along the margin. Continued on page 187.

185

Watch for differences in cell size and shape in different parts of the prothallus. Such features as chloroplast density and distribution within cells should also be recorded.

As the prothallus continues to grow, the appearance of the apical notch (Fig. 13-2C) gives it the characteristic heart-shaped form. This apical notch area is a *meristematic* region, a site of continued active cell division, which adds cells to the growing prothallus.

4. When the prothalli attain maturity, watch for the development of antheridia. While the amount of time in culture required for antheridium formation varies markedly with culture conditions, you may expect to find antheridia after several weeks in culture. They appear as protruberances in the area of the pointed end of the prothallus (Fig. 13-2D).

You can observe the activities of the motile fern sperm by transferring the gametophyte to a drop of tap water on a slide. Focus up and down on an antheridium and look for movements of sperm within it. Some antheridia may discharge sperm spontaneously as you watch or you may be able to facilitate your observations by pressing the cover slip gently. Note the corkscrew shape and somewhat erratic swimming habits of the sperm.

5. In cultures maintained for longer periods of time, there may be complex outgrowths from individual prothalli which can actually produce colonies of attached prothalli. Examine your cultures occasionally for development of more complex growth patterns.

6. Development of archegonia may take a matter of up to several months under these culture conditions. If you maintain cultures for long periods of time, it would be advisable to transfer at least some of the plants to fresh culture dishes. Repeated examination of your plants for archegonium formation probably would damage them. Thus, if you lack large numbers of plants, you simply may need to wait for signs of growth of the young sporophyte plant.

C.

D.

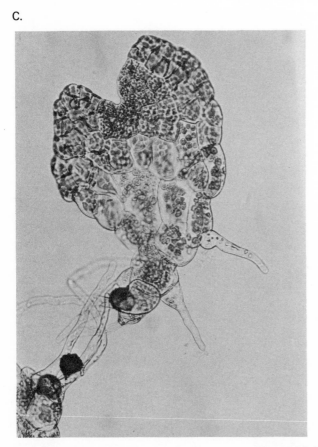
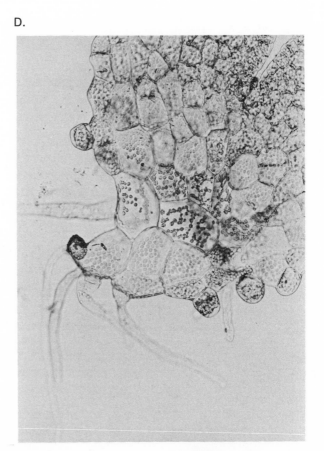

Figure 13-2. Continued.

187

SUGGESTIONS FOR FURTHER INVESTIGATION

Additional general information on techniques for studying fern gametophyte development can be obtained by reading Davis and Postlethwait (1966) and Miller (1968). You may wish to pursue some of the interesting possibilities for further work which these papers suggest. For example, Davis and Postlethwait describe methods for growing fern spores on agar coated slides. This technique makes repeated observation of a single developing plant much simpler than it is in liquid culture. It also permits more critical study of the results of certain experimental treatments such as unidirectional illumination (See suggestions section of Exercise 14 for further information).

For purposes of comparison, it should be mentioned that a major emphasis of developmental studies on flowering plants has been on the growth and differentiation of the sporophyte plant. In fact, in flowering plants, the gametophytes are inconspicuous structures which do not live independently, but rather undergo their relatively simple differentiation as dependent attachments to the sporophyte plants. However, the study of fern gametophyte development is quite relevant to other plant development studies because it presents some of the same basic types of developmental problems. For example, problems of early and clear differentiation of diverse cell types are apparent in the formation of the early filament cells and the first rhizoid. Specific change in cell division plane plays a clear role in fern gametophyte morphogenesis as it does in plant morphogenesis in general. The differentiation of multicellular reproductive organs is analogous to the formation of specialized multicellular structures in flowering plants. Comparisons can be made between the roles of the meristematic region in the gametophyte's apical notch and the apical meristems in roots and shoots during sporophyte development.

The study of the fern life history was historically important in the elucidation of the relationships of the phases of the life cycles of higher plants. The problem of production of two different morphological expressions by a single organism is of considerable interest, and ferns have been used in experiments on the physiological basis of this phenomenon. General discussions of the problem can be found in many botany texts, but some specific background information relevant to ferns is provided by Bell (1959) and DeMaggio (1963).

You might wish to repeat and extend some of the experiments which have been done on various fern life cycle phases. For example, Whittier and Steeves (1960) reported that *apogamy* (the direct production of sporophyte plants from gametophytes without gamete fusion) could be induced in sterile cultures of one strain of *Pteridium* grown on agar-mineral salt medium enriched with glucose. They found that 2.5% glucose was the optimal concentration for the induction of sporophyte development. The apogamous sporophytes ranged from structures which were morphologically intermediate between gametophyte and sporophyte to quite normal-appearing young sporophyte plants. The induction of apogamy in other strains of *Pteridium aquilinum* required higher sugar concentrations and longer periods of exposure. See also Elmore and Whittier (1973).

Apospory (the production of gametophyte tissue without the intervention of meiosis and spore formation) has also been induced in *Pteridium*. Bell and Richards (1958) raised normal young sporophytes in culture. They detached fully expanded first or second leaves, placed them on sterile mineral-agar, and used a small square of glass to keep a portion of each leaf close to the medium. Filaments grew out from the margins or surfaces of these leaves and eventually produced heart-shaped gametophytes. The young sporophytes from which these cultures were initiated were apparently completely normal and microspectrophotometric examination indicated that the nuclei of cells in these aposporously produced gametophytes contained twice as much DNA per nucleus as did the original gametophytes grown from spores. This indicated that the cells of these aposporous gametophyte plants retained the normal diploid genetic complement of the sporophyte generation.

Interesting developmental problems are raised by these abrupt, induced changes from one morphological expression to another which are independent of the nuclear events (fertilization or meiosis) normally associated with the changes. You may wish to attempt repetition of these rather striking demonstrations of environmental modification of genetic expression, and there are a variety of possible extensions of these experiments which could be attempted without too much difficulty.

REFERENCES

GENERAL

BOLD, H. C. 1970. *Morphology of plants.* New York: Harper and Row.

DAVIS, B. D., and POSTLETHWAIT, S. N. 1966. Classroom experimentation using fern gametophytes. *Amer. Biol. Teacher* 28:97-102.

FOSTER, A. S., and GIFFORD, E. M., JR. 1959. *Comparative morphology of vascular plants.* San Francisco: W. H. Freeman & Co.

LAETSCH, W. M. 1967. Ferns. In *Methods in developmental biology,* F. H. Wilt and N. K. Wessells, eds. New York: Thomas Y. Crowell, pp. 319-328.

LEOPOLD, A. C. 1964. *Plant growth and development.* New York: McGraw-Hill.

MILLER, JOHN H. 1968. Fern gametophytes as experimental material. *Bot. Rev.* 34:361-440.

NAF, U. 1962. Developmental physiology of lower archegoniates. *Ann. Rev. Plant Physiol.* 13:465-488.

TORTORA, G. J.; CICERO, D. R.; and PARISH, B. J. 1970. *Plant form and function.* New York: Macmillan.

WARDLAW, C. W. 1952. *Morphogenesis in plants.* London: Methuen. (Barnes and Noble, New York-U.S. Distributor.)

WHITTIER, D. P. 1971. The value of ferns in an understanding of the alternations of generations. *Bio-Science* 21: 225-227. (Five additional papers on "Ferns as Tools in Solving Biological Problems" follow this one. These valuable papers are on pages 266, 271, 313, 317, and 323 in Vol. 21 of *Bio-Science.*)

SPECIFIC

BELL, P. R. 1959. The experimental investigation of the pteridophyte life cycle. *J. Linn. Soc. (Bot.)* 56: 188-203.

BELL, P. R., and RICHARDS, B. M. 1958. Induced apospory in polypodiaceous ferns. *Nature* 182:1748-1749.

DEMAGGIO, A. E. 1963. Morphogenetic factors influencing the development of fern embryos. *J. Linn. Soc. (Bot.)* 58:361-376.

ELMORE, H. W., and WHITTIER, D. P. 1973. The role of ethylene in the induction of apogamous buds in *Pteridium* gametophytes. *Planta* 11:85-90.

STEEVES, T. A.; SUSSEX, I. M.; and PARTANEN, C. R. 1955. *In vitro* studies on abnormal growth of prothalli of the bracken fern. *Amer. Jour. Bot.* 42:232-245.

WHITTIER, D. P. 1966. The influence of growth substances on the induction of apogamy in *Pteridium* gametophytes. *Amer. Jour. Bot.* 53:882-886.

WHITTIER, D. P., and STEEVES, T. A. 1960. The induction of apogamy in the bracken fern. *Canadian Jour. Bot.* 38:925-930.

MATERIALS

EQUIPMENT

Petri dishes (small Erlenmeyer flasks may also be used for culturing gametophytes)
Clean microscope slides and cover slips
Bacteriological loops or pipettes (ordinary "medicine droppers" work well)
Forceps
Small spatula (useful, but not essential for handling older prothalli)
Compound microscope
Light source for cultures (see "techniques" section)

SOLUTIONS AND CHEMICALS

Basic fern medium

LIVING MATERIAL

Pteridium aquilinum spores

Photomorphogenesis in Fern Gametophytes

Because of the role of light as the energy source for photosynthesis, it would be expected that light would be an important factor in the control of plant development. It has been known for some time, however, that light has other direct effects on plant development. These effects are grouped under the collective name, "photomorphogenesis." Mohr has defined photomorphogenesis as control which can be exerted by visible light over growth, development and differentiation of a plant independent of photosynthesis. There are a variety of developmental responses which are dependent upon light intensity, light quality (wavelength) or the relative length of light and dark periods ("photoperiodic" responses). All of these aspects of the nature of illumination must be considered in the interpretation of photomorphogenetic phenomena, and the availability of modern instrumentation has made possible controlled quantitative studies on all of these factors.

Some photomorphogenetic effects on plant development have been known and studied for many years. For example, Darwin experimented on specific plant growth responses to unidirectional illumination. Another strikingly obvious light relationship in plant development which has been under study for more than 100 years is etiolation. It is commonly known that green plants grown in darkness or very weak light tend to be exceptionally tall and spindly. They have small, unexpanded leaves and are very pale due to the arrest of chloroplast development. In at least some plants, very short periods of light exposure are adequate to prevent much of the etiolation effect of growth in the dark. In the prevention of etiolation, as well as in many other photomorphogenetic effects, the most effective part of the light spectrum is in the red region. This red-light responsiveness is mediated by a specific light-absorbing pigment, phytochrome, and can be reversed if the red-light treatment is followed by a period of exposure to far-red light. In some developing systems, phytochrome-mediated responses appear to take the form of developmental "switch" mechanisms which are

fixed in particular courses of development after only one exposure period, but in others, such as the germination of Grand Rapids lettuce seeds, the response actually can be reversed repeatedly by alternating red- and far-red illumination. Further studies at the physiological and biochemical levels have demonstrated that this control is based on the occurrence of two forms of phytochrome which are interconvertible in response to red- and far-red light exposure.

Light also exerts control over the growth and development of fern gametophytes. In some ferns, for example, there are marked light requirements for spore germination. Another particularly obvious light control relationship is in the switchover from one-dimensional to two-dimensional growth. Gametophytes grown in red light continue the filamentous protonemal growth form and do not acquire the new plane of cell division necessary to produce the flat prothallus. However, this abnormal development in red light is due to disruption of complex light relationships and cannot be interpreted directly in terms of the phytochrome model (see "Suggestions" section). Nevertheless, this is an interesting example of photomorphogenetic control in plants and this exercise will introduce you to the phenomenon.

TECHNIQUES

It is important to begin experiments on photomorphogenesis with caution because the experiments suggested here can be conducted at several levels of sophistication, as can all experiments on photomorphogenesis. Accurate measurements of light intensity and spectral qualities are possible when proper instruments are available and the wavelength emission of light sources can be controlled with specially designed filters. If you do wish to make repeatable quantitative measurements leading to firm conclusions about various aspects of photomorphogenesis, it is essential that you employ such instruments and techniques. This is the only sound basis upon which you can make definite comparisons between your results and those reported by researchers in this field. However, you can obtain very useful "qualitative" results even if your work is done at a less sophisticated level and these directions are written at that level. But if radiometry equipment and proper light sources are available, your instructor may ask you to upgrade the level of approach, particularly in terms of measurement and regulation of the total light energy reaching control and experimental cultures.

It would be desirable to make each of the observations in the suggested experiments with large numbers of gametophytes, but you may be somewhat limited by the numbers of plants actually available. Your instructor will make some suggestions about numbers to be used in each case and you will be able to make independent judgments for yourself as you acquire a "feeling" for the material.

A. Growth in Red Light

1. Follow the same procedures that you used in Exercise 13 to set up control and experimental cultures. Your instructor may elect to schedule these experiments simultaneously with your basic observations on fern gametophyte development. In that case, the term "control culture" may refer simply to your initial gametophyte cultures. You must take great care to shelter your red-light cultures from any other light sources because a small amount of "leaked" white or blue light can have drastic consequences for your results. You may provide either a definite photoperiod or continuous illumination for your red-light plants, but you should try to make the experimental and control situations as nearly comparable as possible. Take the same precautions about contamination and fluid level with your red-light plants and use the same techniques to remove plants for examination.

2. Check your cultures at daily intervals and make the comparisons suggested in the "Analysis" section. Consult your instructor concerning the numbers of plants which should be examined each day.

B. Transfer from Red Light to White Light

You should make this transfer when plants in your red-light cultures have at least as many cells as control plants had at the time that they switched over to two-dimensional growth. Your instructor may suggest a specific time for this transfer or may ask you to make a series of transfers at various stages if you have enough plants available. Transfer some plants from your red-light cultures to a new culture which can be moved to the white-light area. Follow the further development of these transferred plants carefully and record the results for comparison with other groups of plants. As a control for this experiment, you also may wish to transfer some plants to fresh medium and leave them under red light.

C. Transfer from White Light to Red Light

As a reciprocal experiment to the one suggested in "B" above, transfer some of the control plants to the red-light area. You should make this transfer after the controls are well into the two-dimensional growth phase. Your instructor may suggest a specific stage or leave this choice to you. A control culture of plants transferred to fresh medium, but left under white light would be desirable.

D. Analysis of Results

It probably would be most convenient to keep results from the several types of experiments separated from one another as you are taking them, but later you will want to combine data of various kinds in different ways for purposes of comparison and discussion.

1. In all cases, record information on:

   (a) Spore germination and early growth of protonemata and rhizoids.
   (b) General appearance of plants (sketches are very useful).
   (c) Number of cells per plant.
   (d) Area of the prothalli.
   (e) Cell sizes, shapes, and other characteristics at all stages.
   (f) Chloroplast density and distribution within cells.
   (g) One-dimensional and two-dimensional growth relationships and the characteristics of the plants at the time of switchover.

2. *Growth in Red Light.* Make the general observations suggested above at a series of intervals. Continue observations on the red-light plants at least as long as it takes for control plants to become well-developed plates of cells. Possibly you and your instructor will agree to carry the observations on for longer periods of time in order to see if the red-light effects can be maintained more or less indefinitely.

3. *Transfer from Red Light to White Light.* In transfer experiments, the time course of developmental responses to the change is of vital importance. Thus, it is essential to record all observations in relation to time since transfer.

The switch to two-dimensional growth involves changes in cell behavior during cell division, but you should be able to record changes in cell shape and possibly in other characteristics which precede the first oblique cell division.

4. *Transfer from White Light to Red Light.* Once again, time sequence is critical and times of all observations should be carefully recorded.

Begin to examine small samples of plants daily after 3 days in red light. Watch for evidence of filamentous growths of the type seen in your initial red-light cultures. If you find any evidence of revision to filamentous growth, examine larger samples at regular intervals. Sketch results and record specific information on changes in cell characteristics.

197

You may encounter a number of difficulties in conducting these experiments, or you may obtain results in one experiment which are difficult to reconcile with those in another, but frequently such difficulties are instructive because careful consideration can provide new insight into the problems of designing, conducting and interpreting experiments on photomorphogenesis. Some of the problems which you will need to bear in mind while examining and discussing your experimental results are: (a) the vastly different effectiveness for photomorphogenetic responses of comparable total light energies at different wavelengths and the actual spectral qualities of light in your particular experimental situation, (b) the interaction of light with other environmental factors, (c) the total radiant energy actually reaching plants in any given experiment, and (d) the question of photosynthetic rates and their bearing on growth rates in various experiments.

SUGGESTIONS FOR FURTHER INVESTIGATION

The details of the transition from one-dimensional to two-dimensional growth in *Pteridium aquilinum* gametophytes have been described by Davis (1969). He studied the sequence of morphological events which followed transfer from red light to white light and examined the effects of various light intensities on rates of change. If you wish to do further detailed work on the reorientation of cell-division plane or other aspects of the switchover, you should consult this paper for a useful basic description and literature citations which relate the phenomenon to similar ones in other plants.

Davis (1968a) designed experiments to determine the minimal length of exposure to white light necessary to induce plants previously grown in red light to switch to two-dimensional growth. Basically, his experiments involved growing plants in red light until they showed the obvious characteristics of red-light treatment, transferring samples to white light for various periods, and returning them to red light. Then he determined the percentage in each group which had entered the two-dimensional phase after their return to red light (actually the difference between the percentage of two-dimensional gametophytes at the end of the white light exposure and at the end of 72 hours back in red light). You may wish to repeat or extend his experiments. Although conditions vary, you might start your experiments with various white light exposures between 12 and 60 hours in length. You can avoid some interpretation problems if you use continuous illumination throughout the experiment.

Discussion of various general aspects of photomorphogenesis can be found in the texts listed in the "General References" section or in various review articles (*e.g.*, in Wilkins, 1969). An important emphasis in these general sources is on the phytochrome system which responds to red and far-red illumination. If you pursue the literature on fern gametophyte photomorphogenesis, however, you will find that the situation in this system is actually quite complex because there appear to be several, simultaneously operative photoreceptor systems (see Mohr in Wilkins, 1969; Miller and Miller, 1967). The elongation of rhizoids in dark-grown protonemata and the rate of cell division in two-dimensional prothallia of some species are controlled by a phytochrome system corresponding to that found in higher plants. But it seems clear that the switchover from one- to two-dimensional growth in *Pteridium* (Davis, 1968a) and other ferns is critically dependent upon exposure to blue light. It has been proposed that riboflavin is the photoreceptor involved in response to blue light (Yeoh and Raghaven, 1966), but further experiments by Davis (1968b) have cast doubt upon this suggestion. You might find it interesting to search through this literature and to repeat and extend some of these experiments.

The initial outgrowth of *Pteridium* protonemata from the spore can be oriented by unidirectional illumination. In addition to experimenting on this establishment of polarity by light, you also may be able to demonstrate a phototropic response in which growing tips turn in another direction if the angle of illumination is changed. For this type of experiment it is virtually essential that spores be shown on agar medium and techniques for doing so are described by Davis and Pos-

tlethwait (1966). Light effects on polarity and orientation of growing plants are discussed in a number of texts, and you might enjoy reading further on these aspects of photomorphogenesis.

As fern gametophytes depend upon photosynthesis to provide them with energy for maintenance and growth, their growth rate obviously is markedly affected by light intensity. Thus, there is some controversy concerning the relative importance of light intensity and spectral quality in the control of the switch to two-dimensional growth in *Pteridium* (compare Sobota and Partanen, 1966, with Davis, 1968a). If you wish to design experiments to attack this problem, you might find the sucrose supplementation experiments of Miller and Miller (1961) helpful (see also Davis, 1971).

It is likely that control of developmental events such as the switchover from one-dimensional to two-dimensional growth in the fern gametophyte ultimately can be explained in terms of cellular genetic expression. But controversy has developed around the results of biochemical studies on the genetic basis for the transition. You will have an opportunity to repeat one of these experiments in the next exercise and some of the pertinent literature is cited there.

REFERENCES

GENERAL

DAVIS, B. D., and POSTLETHWAIT, S. N. 1966. Classroom experimentation using fern gametophytes. *Amer. Biol. Teacher* 28:97-102.

LAETSCH, W. M. 1967. Ferns. In *Methods in developmental biology*, F. H. Wilt and N. K. Wessells, eds. New York: Thomas Y. Crowell, pp. 319-328.

LEOPOLD, A. C. 1964. *Plant growth and development*. New York: McGraw-Hill.

MOHR, H. 1964. The control of plant growth and development by light. *Biol. Rev.* 39:87-112.

STEWARD, F. C. 1968. *Growth and organization in plants*. Reading Mass.: Addison-Wesley.

TORREY, J. C. 1967. *Development in flowering plants*. New York: Macmillan.

WAREING, P. F., and PHILLIPS, I. D. J. 1970. *The control of growth and differentiation in plants*. New York: Pergamon Press.

WILKINS, M. B. ed. 1969. *The physiology of plant growth and development*. New York and London: McGraw-Hill.

SPECIFIC

DAVIS, B. D. 1968a. Effect of light quality on the transition to two-dimensional growth by gametophytes of *Pteridium aquilinum*. *Bulletin Torrey Bot. Club* 95:31-36.

———. 1968b. Is riboflavin the photoreceptor in the induction of two-dimensional growth in fern gametophytes? *Plant Physiol.* 43:1165-1167.

———. 1969. The transition from filamentous to two-dimensional growth in fern gametophytes. II. Kinetic studies on *Pteridium aquilinum*. *Amer. Jour. Bot.* 56:1048-1053.

———. 1971. The transition from filamentous to two-dimensional growth in fern gametophytes. III. Interaction of cell elongation and cell division. *Amer. Jour. Bot.* 58:212-217.

MILLER, J. H. 1968. An evaluation of specific and non-specific inhibition of two-dimensional growth in fern gametophytes. *Physiologia Plantarum* 21:699-701.

MILLER, J. H., and MILLER, P. M. 1961. The effect of different light conditions and sucrose on the growth and development of the fern, *Onoclea sensibilis*. *Amer. Jour. Bot.* 48:154-159.

———. 1967. Action spectra for light-induced elongation in fern protonemata. *Physiologia Plantarum* 20:128-138.

SOBOTA, A. E., and PARTANEN, C. R. 1966. The growth and division of cells in relation to morphogenesis in fern gametophytes. I. Photomorphogenetic studies in *Pteridium aquilinum*. *Canad. Jour. Bot.* 44: 497-506.

YEOH, O. C., and RAGHAVAN, V. 1966. Riboflavin as photoreceptor in the induction of two-dimensional growth in fern gametophytes. *Plant Physiol.* 41:1739-1742.

MATERIALS

EQUIPMENT
Petri dishes (small Erlenmeyer flasks may also be used for culturing gametophytes)
Clean microscope slides and cover slips
Bacteriological loops and pipettes (ordinary "medicine droppers" work well)
Compound microscope
Light sources for control and "red-light" cultures

SOLUTIONS AND CHEMICALS
Basic fern medium

LIVING MATERIAL
Pteridium aquilinum spores

203

Control of Cell Division Planes in Fern Gametophytes

The orientation of cell division planes is an important factor at all stages of development in producing the basic forms of tissues, organs, and entire organisms. If cell divisions occurred with random spatial orientation, proliferation would produce a formless, unorganized mass of cells. Such random growth patterns often are seen in tumors and in many cultured tissues. Oriented cell divisions are particularly significant in plant development because the massive cell migrations which are so important in establishing the early organization of developing animals are lacking in plant development.

In addition to contributing to the production of the basic form of developing organisms, specifically orientated cell divisions play several other types of roles in development of various organisms. For example, mitotic divisions which result in unequal segregation of specific cytoplasmic constituents between daughter cells are important features of development in many organisms. This type of division is seen in the early development of frogs (Exercise 2) and sea urchins (Exercise 10) and in many other organisms. Another related role of specifically oriented cell division is in the establishment of polarity.

The control of the orientation of cell division is a fundamentally important problem in Developmental Biology and it is being studied in a variety of developing systems. It is quite clear that the orientation of the mitotic spindle normally controls the plane of cell division, but recognition of this relationship simply shifts attention to the nature of the mechanisms underlying and controlling orientation of the mitotic spindle.

The early development of the fern gametophyte provides a useful "model system" for an attack on the problem of control of oriented cell division in development. The switchover from one-dimensional to two-dimensional growth is a clear and readily recognizable change in orientation of the cell division plane. Recognition of the importance of light quality in control of the change raises

205

further questions about the nature of the underlying cellular activities which account for the normal switchover and which are altered under experimental conditions.

Experimental tests of the hypothesis that the switchover involves genetic activation expressed through synthesis of new proteins have been undertaken, but disagreements have developed over conclusions drawn by various workers. Because of the controversial nature of this research, only one introductory experiment is presented in the technique section, but the rather extensive "Suggestions" section will point out other approaches to the problem.

Several investigators have found that various analogues of RNA bases adversely affect the transition from the one-dimensional, or filamentous, phase of growth to the two-dimensional growth phase in a variety of ferns. In particular, it has been reported that 2-thiouracil, an analogue of uracil, prevents the switchover from one-dimensional to two-dimensional growth. This inhibition by 2-thiouracil has been interpreted as an indication that RNA synthesis is required for the switchover because interference with the synthesis of new RNA prevented the initiation of two-dimensional growth.

In this exercise, you will analyze the effects of 2-thiouracil on the development of the gametophyte of the bracken fern, *Pteridium aquilinum*. At the outset, you should recognize that various investigators report variable results in experiments with 2-thiouracil and other base analogues and that there is considerable disagreement concerning the interpretation of results in these experiments.

TECHNIQUES

A. Effect of 2-Thiouracil on Fern Gametophyte Development

1. As in the previous exercises (Exercises 13 and 14), sow spores of the bracken fern in petri dishes containing the basic growth medium. The inhibition experiments are to be performed on spores which have already germinated under standard conditions (at room temperature under "white" light), but are still in the one-dimensional (filamentous) phase of growth. Proceed with the experiment when the majority of the filaments are 2 to 3 cells long.

2. Before commencing the treatment with 2-thiouracil, examine several plants microscopically. Transfer them to a slide with a bacteriological loop, apply a cover slip, and examine under low power. Prepare a sketch of a typical protonema, and record the average cell number of several plants.

3. Transfer samples of the one-dimensional plants with a bacteriological loop to each of five petri dishes. The first of these dishes is to serve as a control, containing only the basic growth medium. The other four petri dishes ("experimental") contain the basic growth medium plus 2-thiouracil at four different concentrations (2 mg/liter, 4 mg/liter, 8 mg/liter and 12 mg/liter). Culture all of the dishes under your standard "white-light" conditions.

4. If inhibition continues through one or two weeks of growth in the experimental medium, transfer some of the 2-thiouracil treated plants to a petri dish containing only basic medium (without the 2-thiouracil).

B. Reversal with Uracil

In some analogue inhibition experiments, it is possible to prevent the negative effects of the analogue treatment by supplying an excess of the normal compound. Thus, it is of interest to determine whether a relatively high concentration of uracil will prevent the inhibitory action of 2-thiouracil. This part of the exercise will test the effect of 2-thiouracil in the presence of excess uracil.

207

1. Transfer one-dimensional gametophytes to petri dishes containing the following solutions: (a) basic fern medium; (b) basic fern medium containing 2-thiouracil at a concentration of 8 mg/liter; (c) basic fern medium containing uracil at a concentration of 30 mg/liter, and (d) basic fern medium containing both uracil (30 mg/liter) and 2-thiouracil (8 mg/liter). Culture the dishes under your standard "white-light" conditions.

C. Analysis of Results

1. 2-Thiouracil Treatment. Follow the further development of the plants and record data on cell division rates and the onset of two-dimensional growth. Compare the effects of the various concentrations of 2-thiouracil and interpret differences which you detect. Carefully note the times of all of your observations because a slight delay may be the only effect in some cases.

2. Reversal with Uracil. Record and interpret data on cell-division rates and orientation of cell-division planes for all of the cultures.

SUGGESTIONS FOR FURTHER INVESTIGATION

There are many texts in which you can find treatments of the role of selective genetic activation in development. Information on the role of specifically oriented cell divisions in developmental processes is also available from many sources. Both of these topics are of fundamental importance in understanding development and deserve considerable attention. (See references at end of this exercise and in the General Bibliography.)

A number of experiments have been done to test the necessity of new protein synthesis for the transition to two-dimensional growth in fern gametophytes, but the effects of various substances which interfere with RNA or protein synthesis have been tested with varying results. Unfortunately, additional problems of interpretation arise from different experimental designs used in various experiments and the possibility that somewhat different mechanisms might be operative in various fern species. Thus, it is essential that you read and compare techniques, results, and conclusions in the relevant papers if you wish to design really critical experiments of your own. Miller (1968) has pointed out a number of factors which must be considered in assessing apparent inhibition of two-dimensional growth. His key point is that general inhibition which actually prevents gametophytes from reaching the developmental stage of transition must be separated critically from specific inhibition of the transition itself, but it would be well for you to read this entire paper carefully if you wish to experiment on these inhibitors.

One line of experiments on inhibitors has involved the use of antibiotics which are known to interfere with certain aspects of nucleic acid or protein synthesis. Experiments on *Pteridium* gametophytes have been described by Raghaven (1968) and Davis (1968b) and their papers include references to some other antibiotic studies on various fern gametophytes.

Several different workers have reported effects of RNA base analogues and amino acid analogues on *Pteridium* gametophyte development. Sobota and Partanen (1967) interpret their results as an indication that the analogues affect cell division and growth and that effects on the transition to two-dimensional growth are dependent upon this inhibition. But Davis (1968b) concludes that there is direct inhibition of two-dimensional growth by some analogues. (See Davis, 1968a, for reference to the effect of 2-thiouracil on the transition to two-dimensional growth in *Pteridium*.)

Disagreement about interpretation of experiments with RNA base and amino acid analogues began when conclusions of Hotta and Osawa (1958) concerning relative protein content at the time of transition were challenged by Bell and Zafar (1961). Controversy has continued in this work at almost every stage. For instance, Raghavan (1968) and other workers (see above) have reported positive results in prevention of two-dimensional growth by analogues, while Burns and Ingle (1968) concluded that base analogues had no specific effects in their experiments. This continues

to be an active field of investigation, and the role of RNA synthesis at the time of transition is being studied in further detail (*e.g.*, Burns and Ingle, 1970).

In addition to problems of interpretation concerning inhibition by RNA base and amino acid analogues, further complications arise because varying levels of other compounds can also affect the transition in various ferns (*e.g.*, mannitol—Kato, 1964; ethanol and acetaldehyde—Smith and Robinson, 1969).

In conclusion, it should be obvious that the results of any experiments in this interesting and challenging area must be interpreted critically. Because of the fundamental importance of orientation of cell division plane, you may wish to experiment further on inhibitors of two-dimensional growth using *Pteridium aquilinum* gametophytes or those of other ferns. In *Pteridium* experiments, Davis' (1969) description of the stages in the normal transition is very useful and the notes of caution laid down by Miller (1968) are pertinent to any work on the transition.

REFERENCES

GENERAL

DAVIS, B. D., and POSTLETHWAIT, S. N. 1966. Classroom experiments using fern gametophytes. *Amer. Biol. Teacher* 28:97-102.

EBERT, J. D., and SUSSEX, I. M. 1970. *Interacting systems in development.* 2d ed. New York: Holt, Rinehart and Winston.

STEWARD, F. C. 1968. *Growth and organization in plants.* Reading, Mass.: Addison-Wesley.

WAREING, P. F., and PHILLIPS, I. D. J. 1970. *The control of growth and differentiation in plants.* New York: Pergamon Press.

SPECIFIC

BELL, P. R., and ZAFAR, A. H. 1961. Changes in the level of protein nitrogen during growth of the gametophyte and the initiation of the sporophyte in *Dryopteris borreri. Newm. Ann. Bot.* 25:531-546.

BURNS, R. G., and INGLE, J. 1968. The induction of biplanar growth in fern gametophytes in the presence of RNA base analogues. *Plant Physiol.* 43:1987-1990.

———. 1970. The relationship between kinetics of ribonucleic acid accumulation and the morphological development of the fern gametophyte, *Dryopteris borreri. Plant Physiol.* 46:423-428.

DAVIS, B. D. 1968a. Is riboflavin the photoreceptor in the induction of two-dimensional growth in fern gametophytes? *Plant Physiol.* 43:1165-1167.

———.1968b. The transition from filamentous to two-dimensional growth in fern gametophytes. I. The requirements for protein synthesis in gametophytes of *Pteridium aquilinum. Amer. Jour. Bot.* 55:532-540.

———. 1969. The transition from filamentous to two-dimensional growth in fern gametophytes. II. Kinetic studies on *Pteridium aquilinum. Amer. Jour. Bot.* 56: 1048-1053.

HOTTA, Y., and OSAWA, S. 1958. Control of differentiation in the fern gametophyte by amino acid analogs and 8-azaguanine. *Exptl. Cell Res.* 15:85-94.

KATO, Y. 1964. Physiological and morphogenetic studies on fern gametophytes in aseptic culture. II. One- and two-dimensional growth in sugar media. *Botan. Gaz.* 125:33-37.

MILLER, J. H. 1968. An evaluation of specific and non-specific inhibition of 2-dimensional growth in fern gametophytes. *Physiologia Plantarum* 21:699-710.

RAGHAVAN, V. 1965. Action of purine and pyrimidine analogs on the growth and differentiation of the gametophytes of the fern *Asplenium nidus. Amer. Jour. Bot.* 52:900-915.

———. 1968. Actinomycin D-induced changes in growth and ribonucleic acid metabolism in the gametophytes of bracken fern. *Amer. Jour. Bot.* 55:767-772.

SMITH, D. L., and ROBINSON, P. M. 1969. The effects of fungi on morphogenesis of gametophytes of *Polypodium vulgare* L. *New Phytologist* 68:113-122.

SOBOTA, A. E., and PARTANEN, C. R. 1967. The growth and division of cells in relation to morphogenesis in fern gametophytes. II. The effect of biochemical agents on the growth and development of *Pteridium aquilinum. Canad. Jour. Bot.* 45:595-603.

MATERIALS

EQUIPMENT

Petri dishes (small Erlenmeyer flasks may also be used for culturing gametophytes)
Clean microscope slides and cover slips
Bacteriological loops or pipettes (ordinary "medicine droppers" work well)
Compound microscope
Light source for cultures

SOLUTIONS AND CHEMICALS

Basic fern medium
Basic fern medium with several concentrations of added 2-thiouracil (2 mg/liter, 4 mg/liter, 8 mg/liter, 12 mg/liter)
Basic fern medium containing 30 mg/liter uracil
Basic fern medium containing 30 mg/liter uracil and 8 mg/liter 2-thiouracil

LIVING MATERIAL

Pteridium aquilinum spores

Preparation of Materials
for Experimentation on Frog Embryos

A. Procurement and Storage of Frogs

Adult male and female leopard frogs (*Rana pipiens*), taken directly from hibernation, may be obtained from several commercial dealers in the United States. Frogs in pre-breeding condition can be shipped (air-freight) from mid-October through late March. Female frogs obtained from dealers in late September or early October can be induced to ovulate, but the percentage of fertilization is not high. Therefore, experimentation on frog embryos is best performed during the period between late October and March.

Dealers with large supplies of leopard frogs are found primarily in the north central states, particularly in Wisconsin and Minnesota, and in the Lake Champlain area of Vermont. The following suppliers will ship throughout the country: (a) Nasco, Fort Atkinson, Wis. 53538 (has absorbed the Steinhilber Co.), and (b) J. R. Schettle Biologicals, P. O. Box 184, Stillwater, Minn. 55082; or The Lemberger Co., P. O. Box 482, Oshkosh, Wis. 54901 (Both Schettle and Lemberger are now part of the Mogul-Ed Corporation). In the Vermont area, either one of two suppliers may be contacted: (a) J. M. Hazen & Co., Alburg, Vt.; and (b) Lake Champlain Frog Farms, Alburg, Vt. Other sources of frogs are listed in DiBerardino's very useful article in Wilt and Wessells (1967, see Bibliography).

Upon delivery, female frogs should be stored at 4°C. Male frogs may also be stored at this low temperature, however, maintenance of the males in running cold water (below 20°C) is satisfactory. Place groups of 5 or 6 females in individual 2-quart glass bowls covered securely with wire mesh, or in large, covered plastic containers with drilled air holes. Add a small volume of spring water or de-chlorinated tap water. Tap water should be aerated vigorously or boiled to drive off excess chlorine and chilled to 4°C before use. Change the water 3 times per week. Feeding of the frogs is not necessary during confinement at this low temperature. When females are to be used for the induction of ovulation, they are brought to room temperature and allowed to equilibrate for 1/2 hour before receiving the pituitary injections. The method of inducing ovulation is described in *Appendix B*.

Several suppliers have prepared "pituitary kits" for use in teaching laboratories. One type of kit consists of a vial of pituitary powder (or several preserved pituitaries) and six adult frogs, 4 males and 2 females, while a simpler type of kit includes pre-injected female frogs and male frogs. An instruction pamphlet is provided with the kit. If you prefer to adopt a ready-made kit rather than to procure and store adult frogs on your own, you may obtain the kits from the suppliers listed above as well as the following: (a) Carolina Biological Supply Company, Burlington, N. C. 27215 or Gladstone, Oreg. 97027; and (b) Turtox (CCM: General Biological, Inc.), 8200 Hoyne Avenue, Chicago, Ill. 60620. The "pituitary kits" are generally available from early November to March.

B. Glassware and Culture Dishes

Students of amphibian biology traditionally use glass finger bowls (4 inches in diameter) for maintaining the frog embryos. The larval stages may be reared in 8-inch finger bowls. Relatively inexpensive finger

bowls may be obtained from Carolina Biological Supply Company. The finger bowls are called "Culture Dishes" by this supplier. In recent years plastic dishes have received increasing favor. The Linbro Chemical Company (681 Dixwell Ave., New Haven, Conn. 06511) sells a plastic multi-dish with a fitted cover (model FB-4-NS) which has proved useful in growing frog embryos. Some workers keep the embryos in Syracuse dishes and then transfer the larvae to paraffined paper cups (*e.g.*, Dixie cups). Clearly, a variety of rearing containers can be used.

The operating dish frequently employed is a Stender dish, 51 mm in diameter and 26 mm in height, but Stender dishes of other sizes as well as a variety of other small glass containers may be used. As described in a subsequent section, the bottom of the operating dish is covered with agar, since denuded embryos tend to stick to the glass surface. Wide-mouthed pipettes are used for the transfer of embryos. These transfer ("frog") pipettes are made from glass tubing (outside diameter, 9 mm; inside diameter, 6 mm). A strip of tubing is heated in the middle and drawn out. After cooling, the tapered end is cut at a level which permits an opening having an inside diameter of 1.8 to 2.0 mm. Rubber bulbs (33 mm long with a 6 mm opening) are used to operate the pipettes. Ordinary medicine droppers may be cut off and fire-polished to produce "frog" pipettes.

Other indispensable items are petri dishes, Syracuse watch glasses, and depression slides. Instead of glass depression slides, plastic slides with a central well may be used. Nasco (Fort Atkinson, Wis. 53538) has a suitable plastic culture slide called "liquiloc culture slide (circle)." Quartz microscope slides may be purchased from the Thermal American Fused Quartz Company, Route 202 and Change Bridge Rd., Montville, N. J. 07045.

Sterilization of all glassware in an autoclave is desirable. If an autoclave is not available, the operating dishes may be soaked in 70 percent alcohol for 10 minutes, and then placed in a covered container for at least 12 hours to permit all alcohol to evaporate.

C. Instruments

1. Glass Needles

Very fine needles, made from glass or tungsten, are used for the extirpation and transplantation experiments on the amphibian embryos. During preparation of glass needles, a "microburner" is employed. The microburner is used to give a small intense flame and is essentially a modified hypodermic needle. A piece of 1/4-inch tubing is inserted through a hole in a No. 15 cork. On the top side, the rubber tubing should protrude about 1/2 inch. A No. 18 hypodermic needle is inserted into the tubing. Beneath the cork, several inches down the tubing, attach a screw-type pinchcock. This allows very precise control of the size of the flame. Attach the cork to a ring stand (with a burette clamp) and connect the free end of the tubing to a gas outlet.

The glass needles are prepared from solid glass rods, 5 mm in diameter. A strip of rod (8-inch strip) is heated in the center over a burner. The ends of the rod are pulled apart, or drawn out, when the central portion becomes soft. The connecting thread is then broken apart; each rod thus has a handle of approximately 4 inches long and a tapered tip. The tapered tip is heated over the microburner until the thin piece bends slightly. Then touch the tip of the tapered piece to the back of the hot needle in the microburner. Wait until the glass melts and adheres to the metal needle. At the moment the glass adheres to the needle, pull the glass out in a rapid motion. The tip of the glass should be drawn to a very fine point. The tip should be firm and sharp, not elastic.

2. Tungsten Needles

Many workers prefer tungsten needles, since they are more durable (Tungsten may be purchased from the General Electric Co., Sales Headquarters, 21800 Tungsten Road, Cleveland, Ohio 44117). Pieces of tungsten wire (0.005-0.01 in diameter, *e.g.*, 218 CS, 10 mil tungsten wire from G.E.) approximately 1 inch long, are mounted, or sealed, on a length of glass rod or tube. Pieces of tungsten wire also may be mounted in ordinary bacteriological loop holders to save time when needles are being "mass-produced." If an angled needle is desired, the bent portion of the unsharpened wire should be approximately twice as long as the desired final length of the tapered tip. The tip of the wire is first flamed with an oxygen-gas burner or ordinary propane torch until the wire tip glows "white." A reasonably useful needle can be pro-

duced directly by this heating process. As heating is continued, periodically check the effects of vaporization of tungsten from the tip by examining the needle under a binocular microscope. The degree of taper and the length of the tapered portion can be controlled by varying the length of the portion being heated. Because of the problems involved in further treatment of needles, you may want to compromise on needle quality and use needles prepared by heating alone. However, a smoother surface can be obtained when the tip of the wire is sharpened to a fine point by dipping it in and out of molten sodium nitrite (or sodium sulfite). Extreme caution must be observed in working with the hot bath of sodium nitrite. The hot bath is obtained by melting anhydrous sodium nitrite in a porcelain crucible on a triangle. Molten sodium nitrite is very corrosive; protective glasses and asbestos gloves are mandatory. The surface of the tungsten needle should be smooth, not uneven and pitted. The evenness with which the metal is removed by the molten chemical will depend upon the temperature of the bath.

3. Ball-tipped Glass Rods

Another glass instrument is the "ball-tipped" glass rod. "Ball tips" are used to make depressions in the agar operating surface in which the embryos are held. A strip (8 inch) of solid glass rod (5 mm in diameter) is heated in the middle, drawn out to a slender rod, and broken in the middle. The thin end of each of the two rods is then placed in a vertical position over a Bunsen burner or a microburner. The glass tip will contract into a round ball upon heating. Various sizes of ball tips should be made.

4. Glass Bridges

Transplants are held in place during healing by "glass bridges." These are rectangular pieces of glasses, 3-4 mm wide and 10-12 mm long, cut from cover slips (thickness No. 2) with a diamond pencil. The rough edges of the glass should be smoothed by passing the four edges slowly through the flame of a microburner. The bridges may be bent at various angles by grasping one end with forceps and heating, from below, an area a short distance from the other end. The glass will bend under its own weight. The glass bridge should stand firmly on its two ends.

5. Hair Loops

"Hair Loops" are extremely useful for manipulating the embryo and transferring pieces of excised tissue. A hair loop is prepared from glass tubing (outside diameter, 5 mm; inside diameter, 3 mm). An 8-inch strip of tubing is heated in the middle, and drawn out straight. The large end is flamed shut. Into the narrow end is inserted, with watchmaker's forceps, the two ends of a strand of baby's hair. The loop of hair can be adjusted to the desired size. The insertion of the strand of hair is done under a binocular dissecting scope. The hair is sealed on the glass tube by dipping the hair loop into melted paraffin. The liquid paraffin will be drawn into the opening of the tube by capillary force and will harden subsequently. Pariffin covering the loop itself can be removed by touching the loop to a warm glass slide.

6. Watchmaker's Forceps

Ordinary blunt laboratory forceps are usually made of nickel-plated forged steel. Such blunt forceps will not suffice for work on amphibian or chick embryos. An indispensable tool is the watchmaker's forceps, made of stainless steel and bearing extremely fine tips. When model numbers are specified, the models generally used are No. 3 and No. 5, the latter having the finer points. They may be purchased from a wholesale jeweler's company, certain general laboratory supply houses, or from specialized instrument suppliers (*e.g.*, Clay-Adams, Inc., 141 E. 25th St., New York, N.Y. 10010 or Hamilton Bell Co., Inc., 30 Craig Rd., Montvale, N.J. 07645). Sometimes they are listed as "micro-dissecting" forceps. Laboratory Supplies Company, Inc. (29 Jefry Lane, Hicksville, N.Y. 11801) offers quality Precision Swiss (or Dumont) style forceps ("model C") at more moderate prices. Mogul-Ed (P. O. Box 482, Oshkosh, Wis. 54901) also offers moderately priced watchmaker's forceps.

With use, the points of watchmaker's forceps tend to become damaged. Sharpening and minor repair can be done with an Arkansas stone which has been soaked in thread cutting oil. More extensive repairs can be accomplished with a special "tweezer sharpener" (Vigor Tweezer Sharpener, TW-1000, catalogue number 1008 from Better Equipment for Electron Microscopy, Inc., P. O. Box 132, Jerome Ave. Station, Bronx, N.Y. 10468).

D. Media and Chemicals

1. Ringer's Solution

Fertilization of the leopard frog egg and subsequent development of the embryos can be undertaken in spring water or natural pond water. If local pond water is not available, a satisfactory substitute is dilute, or 10%, Amphibian Ringer's solution. Ten parts of stock, or full-strength, Ringer's solution is added to 90 parts of distilled water. The composition of stock Ringer's solution (as with all solutions, prepared in distilled water using reagent grade chemicals) is as follows:

STOCK (100%) AMPHIBIAN RINGER'S SOLUTION

NaCl	6.60 gm
KCl	0.15 gm
$CaCl_2$	0.15 gm
$NaHCO_3$	0.10 gm (approximately*)
Water (glass distilled)	1000 cc

*Adjust final pH to 7.8 with $NaHCO_3$

The anesthetic ethyl m-aminobenzoate methanesulfonate, may be obtained from Fisher Chemical Company (Cat. No. 9671) and other suppliers.

2. Orcein Solution

In Exercise 1, a procedure is described for staining the chromosomes of the frog. The stain employed is a 2% solution of aceto-orcein and a commercial preparation of the orcein stain obtained from Carolina Biological Supply Company works satisfactorily. However, a staining solution which stains chromosomes more intensively may be prepared from powdered natural orcein obtained from Esbe Laboratory Supplies in Canada (459 Bloor Street, W., Toronto 4, Ontario). Two grams of powdered orcein are added to a mixture (be careful!) of 60 ml of glacial acetic acid and 40 ml of distilled water. The mixture must be *refluxed* slowly for one hour (be sure to use boiling stones!). After cooling, the solution is stored in a well-stoppered, dark bottle. Since this highly concentrated stain will tend to crystallize out, it is desirable to filter it just before use. However, the filtering process may be avoided by the simple expedient of drawing the stain for use from the middle of the bottle with a pipette.

3. Barth and Barth's Operating Medium

The operations on the extirpation and transplantation of embryonic tissues in Exercise 3 may be performed in 100% Amphibian Ringer's solution, but a preferred operating medium is Barth and Barth's medium which consists of three components or stock solutions, shown in the table below:

BARTH AND BARTH'S CULTURE SOLUTION

SOLUTION A		SOLUTION B		SOLUTION C	
NaCl	5.150 g	$NaHCO_3$	0.200 g	Na_2HPO_4	0.0300 g
KCl	0.075 g				
$MgSO_4 \cdot 7H_2O$	0.204 g	H_2O to 250 ml		KH_2PO_4	0.0375 g
$Ca(NO_3)_2 \cdot H_2O$	0.062 g				
$CaCl_2 \cdot 2H_2O$	0.060 g			H_2O to 250 ml	
H_2O to 500 ml					

The unmixed stock solutions are stored in a refrigerator. When ready to be used, the three components are mixed in the following proportions: 50 ml of A, 25 ml of B, and 25 ml of C. Prior to mixing the three together, heat 25 ml of solution C *just* to a boil to sterilize it, allow it to cool, and add 100 mg of serum globulin. Solutions A and B are also brought to a boil over a flame and cooled before all three are combined. This sterilization by "light" boiling will suffice. It is advisable to add the $NaHCO_3$ solution (B)

last, so as to avoid precipitation of the calcium and magnesium salts in A. To reduce further the risk of bacterial and fungal infections, add 100 mg each of sulfadiazine (USP Powder, Lederle) and mycostatin (100,000 units/gm Squibb) per liter of medium.

4. Agar-bottom Operating Dishes

The agar base is prepared as follows: 20 grams of a charcoal (Animal bone black, Matheson & Bell) is added to 900 ml of distilled water in a 1000 ml beaker. Be very careful in handling bone black because it can be explosive. *Keep the dry powder and especially any airborne dust away from flames or sparks.* Bring the mixture to a boil and slowly add 20 grams of agar (Difco Bacto-agar). Continue to boil this mixture for a few minutes. Pour this solution directly into the Stender dishes, quickly cover the dishes and allow the solution to cool. Approximately 15 agar-bottom dishes can be prepared from this one solution. The dishes, when cooled, are stored in a refrigerator until they are ready to be used.

5. Steinberg's Medium, Disaggregating Solution, Reaggregating Solution

Explants of embryonic tissue can also be cultured in Steinberg's medium. The usual buffers are replaced by a Tris-HCl buffer. In the formula below, approximately 2 ml of 1N HCl will bring the pH to the desired 7.8-8.0 range. Tris(hydroxymethyl)aminomethane may be obtained through the Sigma Chemical Company in St. Louis, Mo.

STEINBERG'S CULTURE MEDIUM
STOCK SOLUTIONS

A.   17 gm NaCl per 100 ml distilled water
B.   0.5 gm KCl per 100 ml distilled water
C.   0.8 gm $Ca(NO_3)_2 \cdot H_2O$ per 100 ml distilled water
D.   2.05 gm $MgSO_4 \cdot 2H_2O$ per 100 ml distilled water

In preparing the medium, 10 ml of solution A plus 5 ml of each of solutions B, C, and D are made up to 500 ml with distilled water. Tris (280 mg) is added and the pH adjusted with 1N HCl to 7.8-8.0.

Steinberg's complete medium may be modified into a disaggregating medium by eliminating the calcium and magnesium ions (hence, the solution is made up without C and D above) and adding 60 mg of EDTA.

Lastly, Steinberg's solution serves well for reaggregating cells by supplementing the complete medium with 0.1% bovine plasma albumin, 0.1% human serum globulin (see Jones and Elsdale, 1963, which is cited in Exercise 4) or even (as in Exercise 4) albumin from a hen's egg. Use the "runny" portion of the egg white to make up this solution. Crack the shell into two parts and then grasp the chelaza and pull it and the yolk over the rim of the shell and discard them. Usually the "stringy" portion of the egg white will also be carried along and the "runny" portion will be left behind. The exercise suggests a 1% solution of egg white, but you may wish to make up additional reaggregating solutions with greater protein concentrations. Mix the egg white in by swirling or shaking the solution in a stoppered flask.

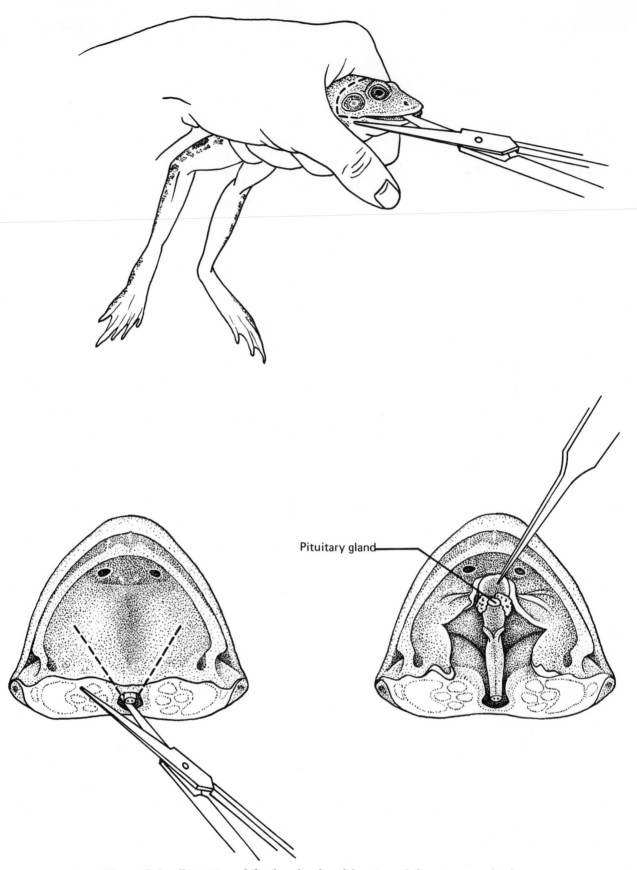

Figure B-1. Dissection of the frog head and location of the pituitary gland.

Induction of Ovulation
in the Leopard Frog

Ovulation in the leopard frog (*Rana pipiens*) may be induced by the injection of an appropriate amount of pituitary glands into the abdominal cavity of the recipient female. The ovulation inducing hormones are contained in the anterior lobe of the pituitary. The recipient female should have been recently collected from hibernation. When received from a dealer, females should be stored immediately at 4°-8°C inasmuch as ovarian eggs undergo degenerative changes at room temperature. Bring the female to room temperature only when she is to be used for the induction of ovulation. Males may be maintained at room temperature at all times.

Fresh pituitary glands, taken from donor frogs, are injected into the recipient female. The pituitary glands of females are twice as potent as those of males. The suggested doses for *Rana pipiens* are as follows:

	FEMALE FROG PITUITARIES		
Oct	Nov-Dec	Jan-Feb	March-April
8	6	4	3

The pituitary gland is located in the cranial floor. It lies ensconced in the *sella turcica,* a cradle-like space hollowed out in the sphenoid bone of the cranial floor. With patience and care, the pituitary gland can be dissected out in its entirety. Figure B-1 will be helpful as a guide in the dissection.

The first step in removing the cranium is to insert one blade of a sharp-pointed pair of scissors into the mouth of the donor frog at one angle of the jaws. Make a cut from this angle to a point just behind the tympanic membrane. Duplicate this lateral cut at the other angle of the jaws. Then decapitate the frog by a transverse cut behind the tympanic membrane and discard the body after the spinal cord has been pithed.

Expose the base of the skull by deflecting forward the oral skin of the upper jaw. Locate the foramen magnum, the large conspicuous opening at the posterior end of the skull through which the spinal cord extends. From this opening, make two oblique cuts directed antero-laterally toward the eye orbits using fine scissors. Deflect the resulting triangular piece of bone forward. Use coarse forceps to lift this flap of bone. The ventral surface of the brain is now exposed. Immediately posterior to the cross-shaped optic chiasma may be seen a pinkish, pear-shaped body, embedded in a white mass of endolymphatic tissue. This pinkish body is the anterior lobe of the pituitary gland. Remove the gland with watchmaker's forceps by grasping the whitish connective tissue surrounding it. Place the whole pituitary gland in 2 ml of full-strength Ringer's solution in a small Stender dish. You may or may not wish to remove the adhering endolymphatic tissue from each pituitary gland removed. These glands will be injected *whole* into the female recipient.

Draw the required number of glands into the barrel of a 2 ml glass syringe and attach a 1-inch, 18-gauge hypodermic needle. Draw approximately 1 ml of full strength Ringer's solution into the barrel along with the glands. The glands will have a tendency to adhere to the wall of the syringe. Gently tap the barrel so as to center all glands over the opening of the syringe. Once all glands fall into the central well of the syringe, maintain the syringe in a vertical position.

Hold the recipient female in your left hand and insert the needle *downward* (as the glands are heavier than water) through the skin and abdominal muscles in the lower quadrant of the abdomen. Exercise care to avoid injury to the viscera. Quickly inject the glands downward, but withdraw the needle cautiously. As you slowly remove the needle, pinch the skin at the point of entry of the needle to prevent any loss of fluid or glands. Finally, draw more Ringer's solution into the syringe to insure that no pituitary material has remained lodged in the barrel of the syringe or in the needle. Re-inject the recipient female with all pituitary material that may have been retained. As the glands pass through the needle, they fragment and form a fine suspension. This facilitates absorption of the hormone.

Place the recipient female in a wire-covered bowl with a small amount of water and keep her at a cool temperature. If maintained at a constant 18°C, fertilizable eggs can be obtained within 36 to 48 hours. At 20°C, ovulation can occur in 30 to 36 hours. At room temperature (about 23°C), eggs can be obtained within 24 hours. Experience shows that best results are obtained when the recipient female is maintained at 18-20°C for 36 to 48 hours.

Recipient females should be tested for the presence of eggs by "stripping" 24 hours after injection and thereafter. The "stripping" technique is described in Exercise 1. If a string of eggs emerges from the cloaca, the sperm suspension can then be prepared. If only jelly or fluid oozes out of the cloaca, retest the female at 12-hour intervals up to 48 hours. If eggs cannot be obtained after 48 hours, a second injection of pituitary is required, comprising half the original pituitary dosage. Such re-injected females should ovulate within 24 hours after the second injection.

Care and Feeding
of the African Clawed Frog,
<u>Xenopus</u> laevis

The experimental manipulations suggested for embryos of the leopard frog (*Rana pipiens*) can be carried out with equal facility on the embryos of the African clawed frog, *Xenopus laevis*. The clawed frog is fully aquatic, both before and after metamorphosis. It can be maintained readily under laboratory conditions, and fertile eggs can be obtained at any time of the year by injecting the female with chorionic gonadotropin. Consult Gurdon's article in Wilt and Wessells (1967, see Bibliography) and New (D.A.T. New, *The Culture of Vertebrate Embryos*, Academic Press, 1966) for further details on the use of *Xenopus*.

Adult males and females will tolerate dechlorinated tap water and can be conveniently maintained in large (20-gallon) aquaria. The volume of dechlorinated tap water generally prescribed is 10 liters per adult animal. Males and females are generally kept separately. The aquarium must be securely covered with a glass or wire lid, since these frogs are adept at jumping great distances out of the water. The frog periodically surfaces for air breathing; hence, an air space is mandatory between the lid and the water surface. No sand or gravel need be introduced to form the floor of the aquaria, although large stones may be added to provide shelter for the animals. Aeration of the water is desirable, but not necessary. The optimal water temperature is 20°C, with a tolerable range of 10°C to 28°C. Extreme temperatures, however, should be avoided.

The adult frogs are fed twice a week with fragments of beef or calf liver. No vitamin supplements are required, but pieces of earthworm and frog tadpoles can serve to vary the diet. Hand feeding is not necessary; the frogs will seek out the food. The water in the aquarium should be changed regularly. Most workers change the water after each feeding period. The clawed frogs are hardy; the mortality rate in the laboratory, with proper care, is exceedingly low (estimated at 2 percent per year).

A female can be distinguished from the male by the presence of cloacal lips, or valves. These are external folds of tissue on each side of the cloaca, absent or weakly developed in the male. During oviposition, the cloacal lips protrude conspicuously and become reddened. Males to be chosen for mating should have darkened "nuptial pads," which are thick streaks of black pigment on the undersides of their forearms.

Mating is induced by the injection of mammalian chorionic gonadotropin into both the male and the female. A relatively inexpensive commercial preparation is "antuitrin S," manufactured by Parke Davis. The hormone solution is made up in full-strength amphibian Ringer's solution, 500 i.u. (international units) per ml. Successful matings are assured by two injections of antuitrin S; the first, a primer, in the morning, and the second, eight hours later, when the pair is placed in the breeding tank. The priming dose is 100 i.u. for the male as well as the female. The second injection, 8 hours later, is an additional 100 i.u. (range: 100-200 i.u.) for the male and an additional 400 i.u. (range: 300-500 i.u.) for the female. The time interval between the final injection and egg laying is usually 8 to 12 hours. Hence, embryos in various stages of development will be found in the breeding tank the following morning.

The hormone is injected into the dorsal lymph sac. While holding the frog in a dry towel, the syringe needle (a No. 22, 1-inch needle) is inserted into the dorsal skin of the *thigh*. The needle is directed forward

towards the subcutaneous lymph space in the back, piercing the septum that binds the skin between the trunk and the hindlimbs. The thigh is the preferred route for injection since the skin of the thigh heals better than the skin of the back.

The male and female will enter into amplexus shortly after the second injection. The male and female, prior to amplexus, are to be placed in a "breeding" aquarium with water at a depth of 6 inches. A plastic mesh, or a wire grid, through which the eggs will drop, should be placed approximately one inch above the base of the aquarium. The mesh prevents the adult frogs from disturbing or even eating the eggs. Several hundred eggs are ordinarily deposited within a span of 12 to 24 hours. The temperature of the water should be between 20°C and 25°C. As soon as spawning has been completed, the pair should be removed from the breeding aquarium.

To avoid overcrowding, the embryos should be removed from the aquarium and placed in individual large 8-inch finger bowls ("rearing" bowls), approximately 10 embryos per square inch in shallow water. When the larvae begin to swim, in a head-downward position within 4-6 days, they are ready to be fed. The larvae are filter feeders, and thrive on a suspension of finely powdered nettle (*Urtica dioica*). (Powdered nettle may be obtained from S. B. Penick and Co. in New York and Chicago.) One gram of the powder is thoroughly mixed in five ml of water to comprise the stock solution. Only a small quantity of the stock solution is delivered into the rearing bowls—an amount sufficient to make the water slightly turbid (about one ml of stock solution in each liter of "rearing" water). The turbidity should be cleared by the larvae within four to five hours. The larvae are fed once a day. The water in the rearing bowls should be changed every 3 to 4 days. Nets should *not* be used as the larvae are susceptible to injury. Transfers to clean rearing bowls may be made with the aid of a beaker.

Within 5 to 6 weeks from fertilization at 20°C, the larvae will undergo metamorphosis, which lasts for two to three weeks. With the onset of metamorphosis (recognized by the eruption of the forelimbs), the larvae cease feeding. The metamorphosing larvae are sluggish and tend to remain at the bottom of the bowl. The water in the bowl must be shallow. When the tail is half resorbed, the young frog, now carnivorous, commences to feed. Small worms (*Tubifex*) or scrapings of liver are suitable daily foods for a postmetamorphic period of three months. After three months, the young frogs are to be provided with a staple diet of pieces of liver. Sexual maturity is reached in 1 to 2 years under laboratory conditions.

REFERENCE

DEUCHAR, E. M. 1972. *Xenopus laevis* and developmental biology. *Biol. Rev.* 47:37-112.

Preparation of Materials
for Experimentation on Chick Embryos

A. Procurement, Storage, and Incubation of Eggs

Fertile eggs may be obtained from a variety of sources in many areas of the country, but the supply and the quality of eggs is often highly seasonal. A first choice for a source probably would be eggs from the genetically controlled lines available in agricultural colleges and poultry research stations. However, good, usable eggs may be obtained from local hatcheries or farmers who keep roosters in their flocks year round. In urban areas, contacts with suppliers of fertile eggs can usually be made through university or hospital virus research laboratories.

Eggs may be stored at about 10°C for up to a week without serious consequences, but longer periods of storage lead to reduced hatchability. Temperatures below 8°C and the desiccating conditions which are normally found in laboratory refrigerators should be avoided. Reset a refrigerator to the higher operating temperature and place a pan of water in it before using it for egg storage. Before incubation, eggs should be removed from the refrigerator and allowed to come to room temperature. Normally, they should be set out in the laboratory at least five or six hours before they are incubated. It will do no harm to allow eggs to stand at ordinary room temperatures overnight, but the length of such pretreatment might influence the amount of incubation time required to bring embryos to a given stage of development.

A variety of commercial incubators are available, but we prefer forced draft models. Sears farm departments can supply good quality 400-egg incubators in a reasonably short order time. The incubation instructions which accompany Sears incubators are good and can be used as an accurate guide to incubation techniques. One such incubator for every 12-15 students would be a desirable ratio but efficient use of incubator space or schedule juggling would make it possible to work with a much less favorable ratio. It is wise to have several replacement microswitches on hand if you use the Sears type of incubator because the high humidity levels cause switches to stick after a period of use with resultant damage to incubating eggs. Once a switch begins to stick, *replace it*. It may seem that working the switch mechanism repeatedly frees it, but it *will stick again* within a short period of further use. Most workers agree that incubated eggs should be rotated daily. Of course, eggs which have been opened for surgery or grafting should not be disturbed after they have been returned to the incubator.

We recommend having and using a candler to sort out sterile eggs, to find dead experimental embryos for removal, and to demonstrate structural relationships to students. Candlers can be constructed, but they are relatively inexpensive at Sears farm departments and other farm suppliers. See comments on candling in section D below.

The vigor and viability of chick embryos varies from one time of year to another. Spring is the best time for work with chick material while work done in late summer or early autumn usually is less satisfactory. If chick work can be delayed until after October 15 in courses taught in the fall term, you will find the results more satisfactory.

Living embryos of the classical commercial stages usually are obtained only after longer incubation times, but you should test this factor in your own laboratory with your own egg supply. The following are approximate incubation times at 38°C (100.4°F) used in our laboratory in the fall of the year:

COMMERCIAL STAGE	INCUBATION TIME
"24-hour" chick	30 hours
"33-hour" chick (12-15 somites)	38-42 hours
"48-hour" chick	55-60 hours
"72-hour" chick	75-82 hours

You may find that embryos will reach these stages after somewhat less incubation time at other times of the year, but the only really definitive answer will come when you test eggs from your own supplier under your own laboratory conditions.

B. Saline Solution

We prefer Howard Ringer solution when an isotonic saline solution is required for use with chick material. The formula is:

HOWARD RINGER SOLUTION

NaCl	7.2 gm
$CaCl_2$ ($2H_2O$)	0.17 gm (0.23 gm)
KCl	0.37 gm
Distilled water	1000 ml

For some routine uses, such as brief examination of living embryos which are to be discarded after use, 0.9% NaCl is acceptable.

There are several other chick saline solutions in use in various laboratories and formulae for them can be found in Rugh (1962) and Hamburger (1960)—See General Bibliography.

Generally, you will obtain better results if the saline solution is warmed to around incubation temperature before it is used with embryos.

C. Instruments and Miscellaneous Materials

1. Instruments

Directions for preparation of the tungsten microsurgical needles and sources for the watchmaker's forceps required in the Chick Exercises are given in Appendix A. Glass microsurgical needles may be substituted for the tungsten needles. Transfer ("chick") pipettes are made simply by scoring, breaking, and fire-polishing ordinary medicine droppers in their tapered portions to produce a finished chick pipette with an inside diameter of 2.5 to 3.0 mm.

2. Egg Nests

"Egg nests" which are used to hold eggs during grafting or embryonic surgery can be made of soft styrofoam. Nine-inch strips of 1/2 inch square styrofoam bent and stapled into a loop make simple egg nests which are actually more practical than more elaborate egg holders such as cotton nests in Syracuse dishes. Eggs are left in these styrofoam nests when they are returned to the incubator following treatment. Sometimes operated eggs can be handled more easily and more gently if the egg nest and egg are set on half of a petri plate. This also prevents fouling of the incubator by poorly opened or accidentally cracked eggs, but the petri plates do occupy more incubator space than the egg nests alone.

3. Egg Saws

Hacksaw blades can be sharpened to make very effective "egg saws." We routinely have used 23 teeth to the inch hacksaw blades, but a variety of other types of blades undoubtedly could serve as well. The blades must be ground on a stone wheel until the teeth no longer protrude outward to the sides, but rather are a straight row of thin, sharp teeth. Some workers prefer to open eggs with rotary dental drills, but the expense of providing several drills for class use does not seem justified when sharpened hacksaw blades work well.

4. Instrument Jars

Instrument jars are prepared simply by placing a layer of compressed absorbent cotton in the bottom of a small jar such as the type in which baby food is sold. The concentration of the ethyl alcohol in the jars must be maintained at higher than 70 percent or it will become difficult to ignite the alcohol when instruments are flame sterilized. Empty baby food jars make acceptable holders for the handle ends of tungsten or glass microsurgical needles if you don't wish to prepare blocks of wood drilled with holes of the appropriate sizes.

5. Alcohol Lamps

While alcohol lamps can be constructed, relatively inexpensive lamps are available from commercial suppliers. Fifty percent alcohol can be ignited, but in practice alcohol lamps are easier to light and they work much more efficiently when filled with 80-90% ethanol. In fact, alcohol concentrations below 70% usually cause problems in alcohol lamps.

D. Candling

If you must make a candler, you can construct one from a three-pound coffee can by cutting a 4 cm diameter hole in one end and mounting a socket for a 100-watt bulb in the opposite end.

Candling should be done in a dark or very dimly lit room, but sometimes candling may be done inside some sort of "dark box" if it is not convenient to take eggs to a room which can be darkened.

There is no substitute for practice in candling eggs, but there are a few points which might be helpful if your experience with candling is limited. These comments describe white-shelled eggs (*e.g.*, White Leghorn), but can be applied to breeds with more shell pigmentation. However, the greater opacity due to shell coloration makes it more difficult to pick out details in candling.

By the end of the *second day of incubation*, it is possible to see some evidence of blood vessel development. However, due to the great variability in developmental stage reached by this time, it is wise to be very conservative about discarding eggs which do not appear to be developing. At the end of the *third day of incubation*, the "spidery" network of embryonic and extraembryonic (yolk-sac) blood vessels is obvious even in eggs with pigmented shells, although there may be some problems with very mottled shells. In white-shelled eggs it is usually possible to pick out the embryonic body and to distinguish the head fairly readily. The sinus terminalis (the peripheral boundary of the extraembryonic circulation) is usually at least faintly visible.

Space limitations prevent detailed treatment of candling characteristics at subsequent stages, but several further comments may prove useful. During succeeding days, you will note the spreading of the vitelline circulation of the yolk sac and the establishment of the chorio-allantoic circulation. The embryo becomes fixed in its position relative to the shell, and shell membranes and the yolk no longer rotate freely in response to gravity when the egg is turned. By about the *fifth day of incubation*, you will notice that the embryo appears to be moving about slowly. This movement actually is due to slow, rhythmic contractions of the amnion which apparently serve to keep the embryo moving about in the amniotic fluid and to prevent adhesions between the embryo and the membrane. Only later will you observe the quick, jerky movements of the embryo itself as neuromuscular coordination begins to become functional. One fairly certain sign that an embryo has died is the presence of a "blood ring." The blood ring is caused by the settling of blood in the sinus terminalis area at the same time that the dead embryo begins to degenerate. This dense, reddish ring without any visible structure in the center is a reliable index of embryonic death from about the fourth or fifth day of incubation onward.

After ten days of incubation, the embryo is quite prominent and has become opaque. It appears as a dark, moving body when the egg is candled. By this time, it is possible to distinguish vitelline from chorio-allantoic vessels. When the egg is rocked, the chorio-allantoic vessels which are closely applied to the inner surface of the shell membrane remain in a fixed position. On the other hand, the vitelline vessels of the yolk sac appear to move about as the yolk shifts slightly in response to rocking.

After twelve or thirteen days, the embryo appears as a very dark object and following two or three additional days of incubation, further growth of the embryo makes the egg seem practically opaque when viewed from some directions. The air space enlarges somewhat during incubation, and by later stages it is prominent and very sharply demarcated in eggs with living embryos. Frequently it is possible to examine the condition of extraembryonic blood vessels which normally appear as continuous dark lines if eggs are tipped or rotated over the candler. In the case of embryos which have died at advanced stages, these vessels appear as broken or irregular lines, but this distinction is sometimes hard to make. With luck, it is also possible to detect the jerky movements of the living embryo, but this becomes almost impossible during the final days of incubation.

Finally, it is well to be very conservative about candling and discarding eggs which contain operated embryos because operated embryos are often smaller than controls of the same age. Because it is possible to be misled by candling, it is well to leave questionable eggs in the incubator for another day or so. Normally, even eggs containing dead embryos decompose only very slowly, and it is unlikely that they will emit enough noxious gases either to be unpleasant to experimenters or to cause damage to nearby embryos in the incubator for at least several days after death.

Preparation of Materials
for Experimentation
on Sea Urchin Embryos

A. Procurement and Storage of Sea Urchins

The most commonly used species of sea urchin in the Developmental Biology teaching laboratory is the West Coast purple urchin, *Strongylocentrotus purpuratus.* It is found in large numbers and has an extensive range from Alaska to southern California. This species spawns in the winter months and may be obtained from dealers from December through March. Experience has shown that the months of January and February are best for obtaining viable gametes. At least two companies in California will provide and guarantee delivery (air freight) of healthy adults. Orders should be placed two to three weeks before the expected date of arrival. One firm is the Pacific Bio-Marine Supply Company (P. O. Box 536, Venice, Calif. 90291); the other is Peninsula Marine Biologicals (740 Tioga Avenue, Sand City, Calif. 93955). Consult Hinegardner's article in Wilt and Wessells (1967, see Bibliography) for information on obtaining and using other echinoderms.

In some cases, adult sea urchins may be kept in healthy condition for up to one week in a cold room, or refrigerator, set at 5°C. They should not be held in seawater. Moist seaweed has been found satisfactory for storage as long as the temperature is kept low (*not* above 8°C). Some other urchin species (*e.g., Lytechinus pictus*) must be maintained in an aquarium if they are to be held longer than one day. Needless to say, it is advisable that the date of delivery coincide very closely with the laboratory exercise on the sea urchin.

B. Artificial Seawater

There are several formulae for the preparation of synthetic seawater. The one used at the Marine Biological Laboratory at Woods Hole is suitable, as well as that devised by Professor Mazia at the Berkeley campus of the University of California. The formulae are presented below. In each case, reagent grade chemicals are used, and the sodium bicarbonate ($NaHCO_3$) is added after all the other salts are dissolved. The synthetic seawater should be made up in distilled water in several liter quantities.

SYNTHETIC SEAWATER (WOODS HOLE MBL)

NaCl	24.72 gm
KCl	0.67 gm
$CaCl_2 \cdot 2H_2O$	1.36 gm
$MgCl_2 \cdot 6H_2O$	4.66 gm
$MgSO_4 \cdot 7H_2O$	6.29 gm
$NaHCO_3$	0.18 gm
Distilled H_2O	To make 1 liter volume

SYNTHETIC SEAWATER (MAZIA)

NaCl	28.32 gm
KCl	0.77 gm
$MgCl_2 \cdot 2H_2O$	5.41 gm
$MgSO_4 \cdot 7H_2O$	7.13 gm
$CaCl_2$	1.18 gm
$NaHCO_3$	0.2 gm
Distilled H_2O	To make 1 liter volume

Several synthetic salt mixtures are marketed. A satisfactory one is "Instant Ocean," prepared by Aquarium Systems (1489 East 289th Street, Wickliffe, Ohio 44092). If necessary, the pH of synthetic seawater mixtures should be adjusted to 8.2.

C. Miscellaneous Solutions and Methods

A solution of 0.5 M KCl in distilled water is used to induce shedding of gametes. (Recall that in expressing concentration in molarity, it is the number of moles of a substance contained in one liter of a solution. A mole is the molecular weight of a substance expressed in grams.) The solution of KCl is to be injected in several points around the peristomial membrane. This will ensure that the solution enters the perivisceral coelom, *not* the lantern coelom. Some familiarity with the anatomy of the adult sea urchin is desirable. On occasion, the injection of KCl may not work. In the event of such failure, the students may have to resort to the tedious, but effective, procedure of surgical removal of the gonads. Methods for stimulating spawning by electric shock also are described by Hinegardner in his article in Wilt and Wessells (1967).

The 0.5 M LiCl used in Exercise 11 is made up in artificial seawater.

The "concentrated seawater" solutions are prepared by dissolving the salts normally used in 1 liter of seawater in appropriately reduced volumes of distilled water (750 ml for 1.5 × normal conc., 500 ml for 2 × normal conc., and 250 ml for 4 × normal conc.).

Some students of Echinoderm development find that temperature control is not so crucial as we have indicated that it is in Exercise 10. In fact, temperatures up to 18°C may be quite acceptable for *Strongylocentrotus* development if clean techniques are used.

243

Preparation of Materials
for Experimentation
on Fern Gametophytes

A. Procurement and Storage of Spores

Pteridium aquilinum (the bracken fern) is a widely distributed species and in many areas it should be possible to find fern fronds with ripe sori if the plants are checked periodically throughout the growing season. The spores themselves may be collected in several ways. Ripe spores remain viable for long periods if they are stored in screw-cap vials and kept in a refrigerator.

A commonly used technique for spore collection is to place fern fronds on large sheets of smooth-surface paper in an area free from drafts which might blow spores away as they fall. If the fronds are left undisturbed overnight (spore drop may continue for several days if the fronds can be left that long) spores will be found on the paper and they can be brushed into vials using a camel's hair brush. Davis and Postlethwait (*Amer. Biol. Teacher* 28:97-102, 1966) suggest that spores be filtered through several layers of lens paper to remove debris, but this step is not essential.

Spores have also been collected by shaking fronds vigorously in plastic bags and passing the materials obtained through a set of soil sieves.

There are several commercial sources of *Pteridium aquilinum* spores. Carolina Biological Supply Company, Burlington, N. C. 27215, or Gladstone, Oreg. 97027, will supply *Pteridium* spores when they are requested specifically under their regular catalogue listing for "Fern Spores." In his "Fern Sources in the United States" (*Amer. Fern Jour.* 52:97-100, 1965), Huttleston lists several suppliers of *Pteridium aquilinum* spores.

B. Media

The relatively simple inorganic medium suggested by Davis and Postlethwait has the following formula:

BASIC FERN MEDIUM

NH_4NO_3	0.5 gm
KH_2PO_4	0.2 gm
$MgSO_4 \cdot 7H_2O$	0.2 gm
$CaCl_2 \cdot 2H_2O$	0.1 gm
Ferric citrate	5 mg*
Distilled water	1000 ml

*0.1 gm of ferric citrate should be dissolved in 100 ml of boiling distilled water and, after cooling, 5 ml of the solution should be added to the medium. The ferric citrate stock solution may be stored for several months under refrigeration.

It is not essential that this medium be sterilized, but autoclave or filtration sterilization might reduce possible microbial contamination in cultures after long periods of growth.

There are a number of other salt solutions which can also be used for growth of fern spores. One of these is Bold's Basal Medium (see p. 87 in *A Laboratory Manual for Plant Morphology*, H. C. Bold, Harper & Row, Publishers). Bill Davis (*Amer. Jour. Bot* 55:532-540, 1968) uses Bold's medium, but substitutes NH_4NO_3 for $NaNO_3$ in the original formula and adjusts the pH specifically to 6.5.

The 2-thiouracil solutions can be prepared by dilution from a stock solution made up in the basic medium. A stock solution with 0.1 gm 2-thiouracil in 100 ml of basic medium is a convenient one to use because each ml of the stock solution contains 1 mg of 2-thiouracil. Thus, 2 ml of stock solution made up to 1 liter with basic medium provides a final concentration of 2 mg 2-thiouracil per liter. Other concentrations can be produced similarly by using appropriate volumes of the stock solution.

A uracil stock solution containing 0.1 gm uracil in 100 ml basic fern medium can also be prepared and used in the same way, but slight heating may be required in order to dissolve the uracil.

C. Culture Conditions and Comments

There are comments on fern gametophyte culturing in the "Techniques" section of Exercise 13, but several other general comments might be helpful.

Generally, cultures are disrupted less if plants are removed with bacteriological loops rather than pipettes.

Very bright illumination induces early transition to two-dimensional growth. If plants become two-dimensional very quickly under your culture conditions, it is likely that the light intensity is too high.

In the photomorphogenesis experiments, red cellophane taped over a flourescent lamp usually will serve adequately as a "red-light" source if "white-light" leaks are prevented. However, you should pretest your particular growth conditions. Filters which transmit light in a well-defined, narrow band of wavelengths are available commercially, but these experiments should work well even under relatively crude conditions. Make certain that any confined area used for parts of these experiments doesn't get too warm.

The results of the 2-thiouracil experiments can be variable and they depend upon a number of factors. Thus, it may be necessary to repeat these experiments using different concentrations or different culture conditions.

Notes on Scheduling and
Use of the Exercises

Individual exercises can be assigned in several different ways for flexibility, but all of the exercises except Exercisce 6 can be done or set up within one weekly 3-hour period. However, some students will need to do extra work in several cases. Exercise 6 is a 3-period lab with work up to section D intended for the first period, section E for a second period, and the remainder of the exercise for a third period. Of course, several of the exercises using living material require an essentially "open lab" approach because repeated observations must be made. The fern experiments can be done outside of regular lab periods, if desired, because the work consists almost entirely of individual observations. Thus, if materials are made continuously available, the fern experiments can be assigned as independent projects which overlap the other exercises. The fern work should be started early in the term so that students will have time to repeat or extend experiments if they wish to do so.

Heavy reliance on live material influences planning of the course during various seasons of the year. For instance, *Strongylocentrotus purpuratus*, the highly-recommended sea urchin species is usable only between December and mid-April. This means that the urchin must be used near the end of a first semester or first quarter course while it is best used during the first part of a second semester course. Some suppliers are optimistic (without justification) about year-round use of frog eggs, but in practice frog work done during September and early October produces very poor results. Finally, there are some problems of vigor and viability in chick embryos during late summer and early fall. Considering all of these factors, it might be concluded that it is not practical to teach a course of this type in the fall. However, the picture is not really that bleak. In fact, one of us (L.G.J.) does teach the course during the fall term. Fern work can provide a good beginning for a fall term course. The chick can be taken up next without undue difficulty, and by the time that the chick section is completed, frog material in good condition can be obtained. The only absolute restriction would be that purple urchins are not usable until December. Inquire in advance as to urchin supply because at least one excellent supplier (Pacific Bio-Marine) shuts down during the pre-Christmas mail rush period.

During the spring, the preferred sequence in terms of vigor and viability of the embryos would be to place the frog before the chick. Fern material could be used anytime, and sea urchins could be used at any point up to the middle of April.

The main point is that you can and should plan your course on an individual basis. There is no substitute for careful planning and scheduling in a course such as Developmental Biology and the rewarding results of concentration on live material will repay the extra efforts many times over.

As a general rule, students will use greater quantities of solutions than you might expect. If you make an estimate of the amount of saline solution needed in one of the chick exercises, for example, it might be well to prepare a 50 percent greater quantity. Experience in your own laboratory will clarify matters of preparation and a complete and regularly revised preparation notebook saves times and effort in subsequent years.

Live material laboratories are "live" laboratories and our goal has been to provide information and assistance necessary to help you to make this approach "go" in your laboratory. If you feel that the information in the Manual itself or in the Appendices is inadequate, please feel free to write or call one of us for advice. Generally, questions concerning Amphibian work should be directed to E.P.V. and other questions should go to L.G.J.

Leland G. Johnson
Department of Biology
Augustana College
Sioux Falls, South Dakota 57102
Telephone 605-336-4714

E. Peter Volpe
Department of Biology
Tulane University
New Orleans, Louisiana 70118
Telephone 504-865-6229

Developmental Biology: Selected General Bibliography

TEXTS IN DEVELOPMENT BIOLOGY

ALSTON, R. E. 1967. *Cellular continuity and development.* Glenview, Illinois: Scott, Foresman and Co. (P).

AREY, L. B. 1965. *Developmental anatomy.* 7th ed. Philadelphia: W. B. Saunders, Co.

BALINSKY, B. I. 1970. *An introduction to embryology.* 3rd ed. Philadelphia: W. B. Saunders, Co.

BARTH, L. J. 1964. *Development: selected topics.* Reading, Mass.: Addison-Wesley Publ. Co. (P).

BERRILL, N. J. 1971. *Developmental biology.* New York: McGraw-Hill.

BODEMER, C. W. 1968. *Modern embryology.* New York: Holt, Rinehart and Winston, Inc.

EBERT, J. D., and SUSSEX, I. M. 1970. *Interacting systems in development.* 2d ed. New York: Holt, Rinehart and Winston, Inc. (P).

FOGG, G. E. 1970. *The growth of plants.* Baltimore: Penguin Books. (P).

GALSTON, A. W., and DAVIES, P. J. 1970. *Control mechanisms in plant development.* Englewood Cliffs, N.J.: Prentice-Hall, Inc. (P).

GILCHRIST, F. G. 1968. *A survey of embryology.* New York: McGraw-Hill Book Co.

GOTTLIEB, F. J. 1966. *Developmental genetics.* New York: Reinhold Publ. Corp. (P).

KERR, N. S. 1967. *Principles of development.* Dubuque, Iowa: Wm. C. Brown Company Publishers. (P).

LEOPOLD, A. C. 1964. *Plant growth and development.* New York: McGraw-Hill Book Co.

MARKERT, C. L., and URSPRUNG, H. 1971. *Developmental genetics.* Englewood Cliffs, N. J.: Prentice-Hall, Inc. (P).

SAUNDERS, J. W., JR. 1968. *Animal Morphogenesis.* New York: The Macmillan Co. (P).

———. 1970. *Patterns and principles of animal development.* New York: The Macmillan Co.

SINNOTT, E. W. 1960. *Plant morphogenesis.* New York: McGraw-Hill Book Co.

SPRATT, N. T., JR. 1964. *Introduction to cell differentiation.* New York: Reinhold Publ. Corp. (P).

SPRATT, N. T., JR. 1971. *Development biology.* Belmont, Calif.: Wadsworth Publ. Co.

STEWARD, F. C. 1968. *Growth and organization in plants.* Reading, Mass.: Addison-Wesley Publ. Co.

SUSSMAN, M. 1973. *Developmental Biology: its cellular and molecular foundations.* Englewood Cliffs, N. J.: Prentice-Hall, Inc. (P).

TORREY, J. G. 1967. *Development in flowering plants.* New York: The Macmillan Co. (P).

TRINKAUS, J. P. 1969. *Cells into organs.* Englewood Cliffs, N. J.: Prentice-Hall, Inc. (P).

WADDINGTON, C. H. 1966. *Principles of development and differentiation.* New York: The Macmillan Co. (P).

WARDLAW, C. W. 1968. *Morphogenesis in plants.* 2d ed. London: Methuen, (Barnes and Noble, N. Y.-U.S. Dist.).

WAREING, P. F., and PHILLIPS, I. D. J. 1970. *The control of growth and differentiation in plants.* New York: Pergamon Press. (P).

*The designation "(P)" indicates that the book is available as a paperback.

EXPERIMENTAL LAB BOOKS

BOLD, H. C. 1967. *A laboratory manual for plant morphology.* New York: Harper and Row, Publishers.

COSTELLO, D. P. *et. al.* 1957. *Methods for obtaining and handling marine eggs and embryos.* Woods Hole, Mass.: Marine Biological Laboratory.

HAMBURGER, V. 1960. *A manual of experimental embryology.* rev. ed. Chicago: University of Chicago Press.

RUGH, R. 1962. *Experimental embryology.* 3rd ed. Minneapolis: Burgess Publishing Co.

VANABLE, J. W., JR., and CLARK, J. H. 1968. *Developmental biology.* Minneapolis: Burgess Publishing Co.

WILT, F. H., and WESSELLS, N. K. 1967. *Methods in developmental biology.* New York: Thomas Y. Crowell Co.

COLLECTIONS OF RESEARCH PAPERS

BELL, E. ed. 1967. *Molecular and cellular aspects of development.* rev. ed. New York: Harper and Row, Publishers. (P).

FLICKINGER, R. A. ed. 1966. *Developmental biology.* Dubuque, Iowa: Wm. C. Brown Company Publishers. (P).

HILLMAN, W. S. 1970. *Papers in plant physiology.* New York: Holt, Rinehart and Winston, Inc.

LAETSCH, W. M., and CLELAND, R. E. eds. 1967. *Papers on plant growth and development.* Boston: Little, Brown and Co. (P).

LOOMIS, W. F., JR. ed. 1970. *Papers on regulation of gene activity during development.* New York: Harper and Row, Publishers. (P).

WHITTAKER, J. R. ed. 1968. *Cellular differentiation.* Belmont, Calif.: Dickenson Publ. Co., Inc. (P).

WILLIER, B. H. and OPPENHEIMER, J. M. eds. 1964. *Foundations of experimental embryology.* Englewood Cliffs, N. J.: Prentice-Hall, Inc.

SINGLE SYMPOSIUM VOLUMES OR COLLECTIONS OF REVIEWS

BEERMANN, W. *et al.* eds. 1966. *Cell differentiation and morphogenesis.* Amsterdam: North Holland Publishing Co.

CUTTER, E. G. ed. 1966. *Trends in plant morphogenesis.* London: Longman's, Green and Co., (Wiley, N.Y.-U. S. Dist.).

DeHAAN, R. L., and URSPRUNG, H. eds. 1965. *Organogenesis.* New York: Holt, Rinehart and Winston, Inc.

McELROY, W. D., and GLASS, B. eds. 1958. *The chemical basis of development.* Baltimore: The Johns Hopkins Press.

WILKINS, M. B. ed. 1969. *The physiology of plant growth and development.* New York: McGraw-Hill Book Co.

WILLIER, B. H.; WEISS, P. A.; and HAMBURGER, V. eds. 1955. *Analysis of development.* Philadelphia: W. B. Saunders Co.

REVIEW SERIES

ABERCROMBIE, M.; BRACHET, J.; and KING, T. J. current eds. 1961-1973. vols. I-X. *Advances in morphogenesis.* New York: Academic Press.

MONROY, A., and MOSCONA, A. A. eds. 1966-1972, vols. I-VII. *Current topics in developmental biology.* New York: Academic Press.

Various Editors. 1939-1970, vols. I-XXIX. *Symposia of the society for developmental biology.* New York: Academic Press.

WEBER, R. ed. 1965-1967, vols. I-II. *The biochemistry of animal development.* New York: Academic Press.

REVIEW SERIES CONTAINING SOME DEVELOPMENT PAPERS

Annual review of plant physiology

Biological reviews

Botanical review

International review of cytology

Quarterly review of biology

Symposia of the society for experimental biology